TABLE OF CONTENTS

For Beginning/Preproduction and Early Production/Speech Emergent stages of English Language Development

These blackline masters are grouped by parts of speech to correspond with the grammar units in *Houghton Mifflin English.* Also included are special sections of General and Multipurpose visuals.

GENERAL USE

Nouns and Pronouns

Verbs

Multipurpose visuals

Adjectives

The blackline masters in this section correspond to the organization of the grammar units in *Houghton Mifflin English.*

- The Sentence
- Nouns
- Verbs
- Adjectives
- Capitalization and Punctuation
- Adverbs
- Pronouns
- Prepositions and Prepositional Phrases

Answer Key for Section 2 Activity Masters

Introduction

Overview of the Students Acquiring English Practice Book

This Practice Book, together with the notes for Students Acquiring English that appear throughout the *Houghton Mifflin English* Teacher's Edition, offers support for teaching grammar skills and concepts to students with varying levels of English proficiency.

Section 1 Activity Masters

The Activity Masters in this section are specifically designed for use with students whose level of English proficiency is at approximately the **Beginning/Preproduction** and **Early Production/Speech Emergent** stages. The masters are grouped by parts of speech to correspond with the grammar units in *Houghton Mifflin English*. Each one is accompanied by teaching suggestions. In addition, special sections of *General* and *Multipurpose* visuals are included at key points to encourage fluency of expression.

Section 2 Activity Masters

The Activity Masters in this section are specifically designed for use with students who are at the **Intermediate** and **Advanced** stages of English proficiency. This second set of blackline masters corresponds to the organization of the grammar units in the pupil books of *Houghton Mifflin English:*

- The Sentence
- Nouns
- Verbs
- Adjectives
- Capitalization and Punctuation
- Adverbs
- Pronouns
- Prepositions and Prepositional Phrases

There are two blackline master pages for every grammar lesson; one page accompanies the *Try It Out* exercise in the pupil book; the other page accompanies the *On Your Own* activity.

Determining English Language Proficiency

The chart below offers information that will help you identify a student's approximate level of English proficiency. A set of characteristic behaviors is described for each level of language proficiency:

Proficiency Levels in English			
Beginning/ Preproduction	**Early Production/ Speech Emergence**	**Intermediate**	**Advanced**
• limited or no understanding of English • rarely uses English for communication except for single words or simple phrases • responds nonverbally to simple commands, statements, questions • constructs meaning primarily from nonprint features • able to generate simple written material but with invented spellings, grammatical inaccuracies, structure and rhetorical patterns from native language	• limited understanding of everyday speech patterns • uses English for a few daily situations • uses simple one- or two-word responses to simple commands, statements, questions • encounters difficulty comprehending complex structures and academic language • constructs meaning from nonprint features and from print features where there is sufficient background knowledge • able to generate simple written material but with considerable numbers of errors	• understands more complex speech but requires repetition • has acquired sufficient vocabulary for many daily situations • uses English spontaneously but lacks sufficient vocabulary and structures to express all thoughts • uses comprehensible, appropriate sentences that still often have grammatical errors • generally encounters difficulty comprehending and producing complex structures and academic language • ability to construct meaning varies considerably depending on familiarity and prior experience with themes, concepts, genre, characters • most successful constructing meaning when there is background knowledge • able to generate more complex, more coherent written material but with considerable numbers of errors	• possesses language skills adequate for everyday situations but some vocabulary and grammar problems remain • may have difficulty using and understanding idioms, figures of speech, and multiple-meaning words • uses English to communicate in new settings • may have difficulty with complex structures and abstract concepts • able to read with considerable fluency • able to locate specific facts within text • may have difficulty understanding text with concepts that are not contextualized, complex sentence structure, or abstract vocabulary • reads independently but may have comprehension problems • able to generate written material independently for personal and academic purposes and with structures, vocabulary, and organization that approaches the writing of a native speaker

(Adapted from *ESL Standards for Pre-K–12 Students,* TESOL, 1997, pages 20–21.)

Effective Strategies for Teaching Students Acquiring English

The teaching strategies and questioning techniques described below can help you better assess and encourage students' English language development. Characteristic responses from students at each level of English proficiency are also shown.

Teacher Strategies

Beginning/Preproduction

- Use natural speech, but with basic vocabulary and sentence structure.
- Use a native-to-nonnative tone.
- Use physical actions and visual clues (pictures, objects) to reinforce meaning.
- Model students' expected behavior and responses.
- Repeat featured vocabulary, giving emphasis through repetition and intonation.
- Focus students' attention on the correct response by modeling and rephrasing.

Intermediate

- Use natural speech with a simplified tone.
- Use visual clues (pictures, objects) to reinforce meaning.
- Repeat featured vocabulary, giving emphasis through repetition and intonation.
- Do not dwell on errors. Instead, focus students' attention on correct response by modeling and rephrasing.

Early Advanced

- Use natural speech with a simplified tone.
- Continue using visual clues to reinforce meaning and repetition of featured vocabulary.
- Teacher behavior at this level should consist mostly of selecting and describing situations that require students to experiment with and use the language.

Teacher Questions

Beginning

- Use commands to encourage physical responses that demonstrate understanding of vocabulary and/or ask questions that require one or two words:

  Point to the....

  Is this a notebook? *(yes/no response)*

  What can we buy at the market? *(listing response)*
- Students may also be asked to draw, cut and paste, or act out activities.

Early Intermediate

- Ask questions that can be answered with phrases or simple sentences:

  How are these items alike/different? Why?

  Tell about your favorite....

  Which of these objects is...?

Intermediate

- Ask questions that require answering in complex sentences and move students toward fluent speech.

  What would you do if...?

  Tell about the time you....

  Do you think that...?

Early Advanced

- Ask questions to encourage and guide discussion:

  What conclusions can you draw?

  Why do you think they did this?

  Do you think this is fair? Why?
- Encourage students to elaborate by asking "Why?" and other open-ended questions.

Student Responses

Beginning

- Students are able to show comprehension through physical responses or with one- or two-word answers: yes or no, either/or, naming of items, listing, common expressions, and completion of open-ended sentences.
- Students may draw, cut and paste, or act out situations to show comprehension.

Early Intermediate

- Students are able to respond to questions with natural-sounding phrases or simple sentences. They can generate original responses. Though students may make errors, they will be able to communicate with meaning.

Intermediate

- Students are able to participate in social conversations and school-related activities using consistently standard English even though they may make some grammatical errors.

Early Advanced

- Students are able to produce fluent speech. They can conduct casual conversations, academic and problem-solving discussions, debates, interviews, and extensive dialogues.

Assessing Students' Progress

You will find Student Assessment Checklists on the pages that follow. These checklists are blackline masters that you can use to measure a student's progress in acquiring English. Use the checklists at regular intervals, but don't feel that you must check all categories during each observation.

Student Assessment Checklist

Student's Name: ______________________________ Date: ______________

Theme/Selection: ______________________________

Student Activities: ______________________________

Language Proficiency Level: ❑ Preproduction ❑ Early Production

To evaluate students' progress, observe behaviors at different times. Use a plus (+) or a minus (-) symbol to indicate that the student has or has not successfully exhibited the behavior.

	Observations	Comments
Preproduction		
Comprehends simple repeated sentences.		
Follows simple 1- or 2-step directions.		
Responds nonverbally by gesturing and by imitating.		
Follows along during picture walks.		
Uses illustrations and other graphic clues to comprehend printed material.		
Illustrates to convey meaning.		
Early Production		
Comprehends simple text.		
Uses everyday, basic vocabulary.		
Makes short, appropriate oral responses to questions.		
Recites poems, songs, and chants.		
Shows comprehension by using one or two words.		
Begins to follow group discussions.		
Follows text during group reading.		
Matches written words to some objects, people, and actions.		
Uses pictures, objects to retell stories.		
Labels illustrations of objects, people, and actions.		
Writes names and simple words.		
Uses temporary spelling, rebuses, and illustrations to convey ideas.		

Comments: ______________________________

Student Assessment Checklist

Student's Name: ______________________ **Date:** __________

Theme/Selection: ______________________

Student Activities: ______________________

Language Proficiency Level: ❑ **Preproduction** ❑ **Early Production**

To evaluate students' progress, observe behaviors at different times. Use a plus (+) or a minus (-) symbol to indicate that the student has or has not successfully exhibited the behavior.

	Observations	Comments
Speech Emergent		
Understands most of what is said with frequent pauses.		
Comprehends stories read aloud.		
Follows a series of directions.		
Speaks in phrases or simple sentences.		
Engages in dialogues and role-plays.		
Takes part in discussions.		
Uses context and decoding skills.		
Reads aloud simple texts.		
Identifies characters.		
Identifies main ideas.		
Writes from dictation.		
Writes simple sentences using details.		
Completes cloze and story frames.		
Intermediate Fluency		
Understands what is said with occasional repetition.		
Comprehends stories and nonfiction selections at grade level.		
Engages in nearly fluent conversation.		
Expresses feelings and experiences.		
Formulates and asks questions.		
Reads aloud and silently.		
Identifies story elements.		
Begins to recognize idioms.		
Paraphrases.		
Begins writing to describe, inform, persuade.		
Uses correct grammar and mechanics.		

Comments: ______________________

Support for Students Acquiring English in the *Houghton Mifflin English* Teacher's Editions

Purpose of the Students Acquiring English notes

You will find special notes and activities for students acquiring English throughout the *Houghton Mifflin English* Teacher's Edition. They are designed to accommodate the needs of students acquiring English at various levels of proficiency. These notes contain information that will help

- familiarize students with the academic language of the classroom
- build background in culture and vocabulary
- identify potentially challenging areas in language and culturally specific content
- focus on grammar elements that are most problematic and/or salient for students learning English
- suggest ways that students can share their rich and diverse cultural and language backgrounds with the whole class
- provide varied options for grouping within the classroom
- provide suggestions for additional practice

1 Use the ***Meeting Individual Needs*** notes for Students Acquiring English to assess what students know and to build background in grammar and vocabulary.

2 **Incorporate** the information in the ***Try It Out*** notes for Students Acquiring English as part of your presentation of the grammar.

3 Use the ***Try It Out Practice*** pages for Students Acquiring English before proceeding with the Try It Out activities in the pupil book. The sentences on these Practice pages are included on audiotape to provide extra practice developing listening skills.

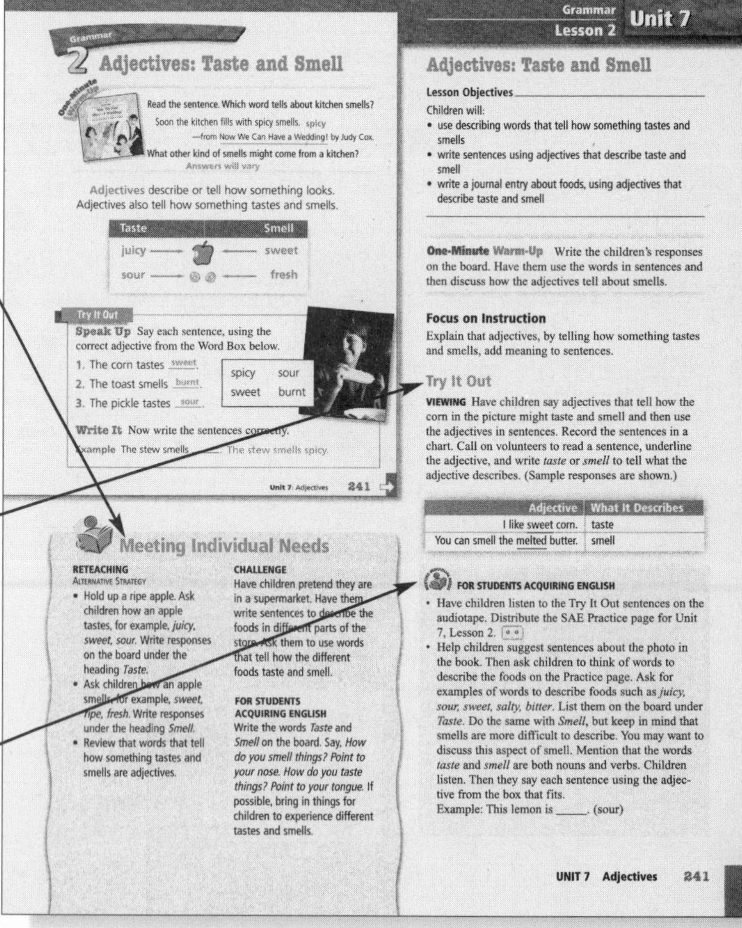

Grammar

2 Adjectives: Taste and Smell

One-Minute Warm-Up

Read the sentence. Which word tells about kitchen smells?

Soon the kitchen fills with spicy smells. spicy

—from Now We Can Have a Wedding! by Judy Cox

What other kind of smells might come from a kitchen?

Answers will vary

Adjectives describe or tell how something looks. Adjectives also tell how something tastes and smells.

Taste	Smell
juicy →	← sweet
sour →	← fresh

Try It Out

Speak Up Say each sentence, using the correct adjective from the Word Box below.

1. The corn tastes sweet.
2. The toast smells burnt.
3. The pickle tastes sour.

spicy sour sweet burnt

Write It Now write the sentences correctly.

Example The stew smells ____. The stew smells spicy.

Unit 7: Adjectives 241

Meeting Individual Needs

RETEACHING
Alternative Strategy
- Hold up a ripe apple. Ask children how an apple tastes, for example, *juicy, sweet, sour.* Write responses on the board under the heading *Taste.*
- Ask children how an apple smells, for example, *sweet, ripe, fresh.* Write responses under the heading *Smell.*
- Review that words that tell how something tastes and smells are adjectives.

CHALLENGE
Have children pretend they are in a supermarket. Have them write sentences to describe the foods in different parts of the store. Ask them to use words that tell how the different foods taste and smell.

FOR STUDENTS ACQUIRING ENGLISH
Write the words *Taste* and *Smell* on the board. Say, *How do you smell things? Point to your nose. How do you taste things? Point to your tongue.* If possible, bring in things for children to experience different tastes and smells.

Grammar Lesson 2 Unit 7

Adjectives: Taste and Smell

Lesson Objectives

Children will:
- use describing words that tell how something tastes and smells
- write sentences using adjectives that describe taste and smell
- write a journal entry about foods, using adjectives that describe taste and smell

One-Minute Warm-Up Write the children's responses on the board. Have them use the words in sentences and then discuss how the adjectives tell about smells.

Focus on Instruction

Explain that adjectives, by telling how something tastes and smells, add meaning to sentences.

Try It Out

VIEWING Have children say adjectives that tell how the corn in the picture might taste and smell and then use the adjectives in sentences. Record the sentences in a chart. Call on volunteers to read a sentence, underline the adjective, and write *taste* or *smell* to tell what the adjective describes. (Sample responses are shown.)

Adjective	What It Describes
I like sweet corn.	taste
You can smell the melted butter.	smell

FOR STUDENTS ACQUIRING ENGLISH
- Have children listen to the Try It Out sentences on the audiotape. Distribute the SAE Practice page for Unit 7, Lesson 2.
- Help children suggest sentences about the photo in the book. Then ask children to think of words to describe the foods on the Practice page. Ask for examples of words to describe foods such as *juicy, sour, sweet, salty, bitter.* List them on the board under *Taste.* Do the same with *Smell*, but keep in mind that smells are more difficult to describe. You may want to discuss this aspect of smell. Mention that the words *taste* and *smell* are both nouns and verbs. Children listen. Then they say each sentence using the adjective from the box that fits.
Example: This lemon is _____. (sour)

UNIT 7 Adjectives 241

How the Students Acquiring English notes relate to the blackline masters in this book

You can use the Activity Masters in **Section 1** with individual students or with small groups of English language learners as you work through the units in *Houghton Mifflin English* with the whole class.

The Activity Masters in **Section 2** are more directly connected to the core grammar lessons presented in the Teacher's Editions.The diagram below shows the relationship between the Students Acquiring English notes in the Teacher's Edition and these blackline masters.

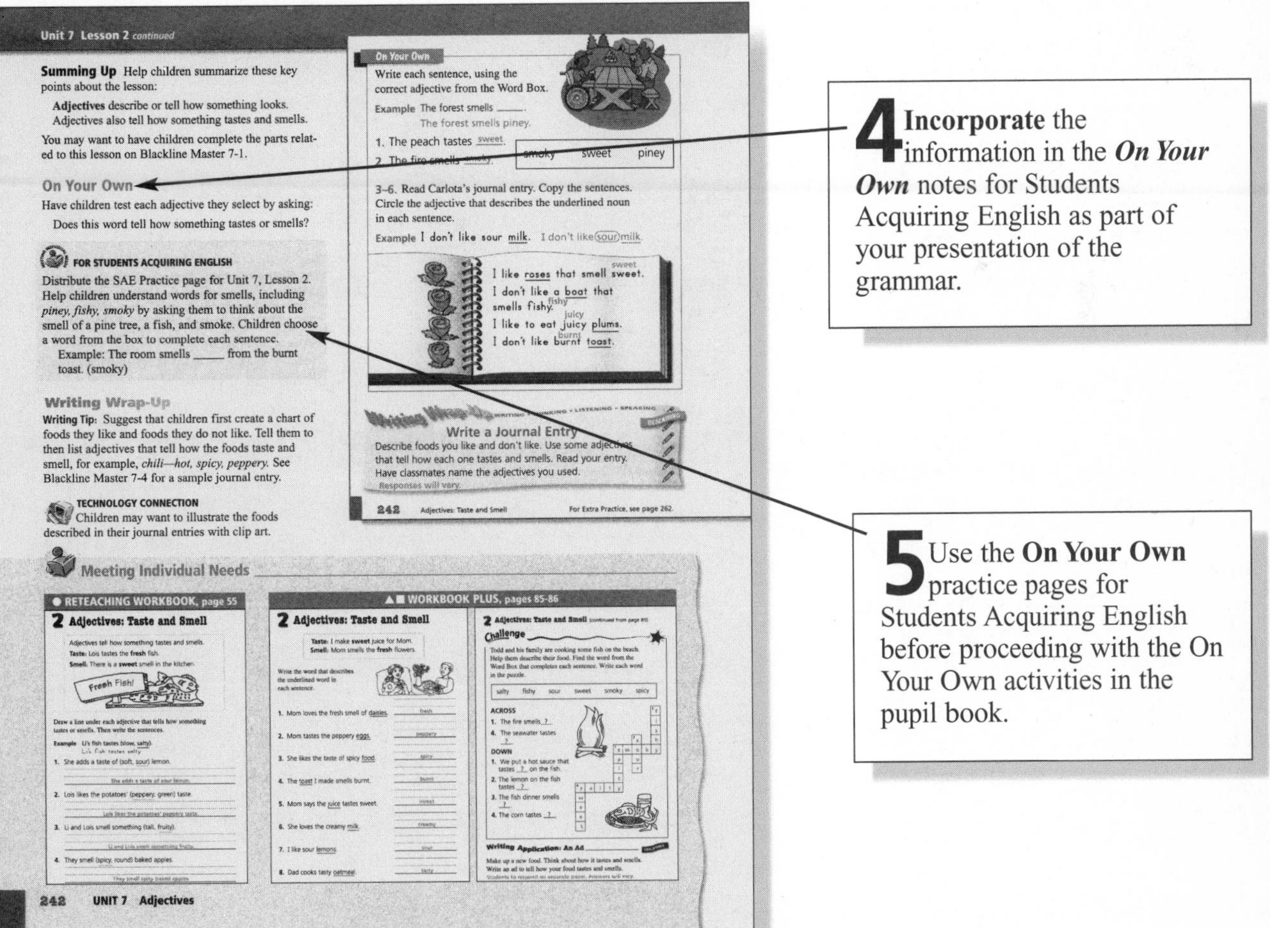
Unit 7 Lesson 2 *continued*

Summing Up Help children summarize these key points about the lesson:

Adjectives describe or tell how something looks. Adjectives also tell how something tastes and smells.

You may want to have children complete the parts related to this lesson on Blackline Master 7-1.

On Your Own

Have children test each adjective they select by asking: Does this word tell how something tastes or smells?

FOR STUDENTS ACQUIRING ENGLISH

Distribute the SAE Practice page for Unit 7, Lesson 2. Help children understand words for smells, including *piney, fishy, smoky* by asking them to think about the smell of a pine tree, a fish, and smoke. Children choose a word from the box to complete each sentence. Example: The room smells _____ from the burnt toast. (smoky)

Writing Wrap-Up

Writing Tip: Suggest that children first create a chart of foods they like and foods they do not like. Tell them to then list adjectives that tell how the foods taste and smell, for example, *chili—hot, spicy, peppery.* See Blackline Master 7-4 for a sample journal entry.

TECHNOLOGY CONNECTION Children may want to illustrate the foods described in their journal entries with clip art.

On Your Own

Write each sentence, using the correct adjective from the Word Box.

Example The forest smells _____. The forest smells piney.

1. The peach tastes sweet.
2. The fire smells smoky.

smoky	sweet	piney

3–6. Read Carlota's journal entry. Copy the sentences. Circle the adjective that describes the underlined noun in each sentence.

Example I don't like sour milk. I don't like (sour) milk.

I like roses that smell sweet.
I don't like a boat that smells fishy.
I like to eat juicy plums.
I don't like burnt toast.

Writing Wrap-Up

Write a Journal Entry

Describe foods you like and don't like. Use some adjectives that tell how each one tastes and smells. Read your entry. Have classmates name the adjectives you used.

Responses will vary.

242 Adjectives: Taste and Smell — For Extra Practice, see page 262.

Meeting Individual Needs

RETEACHING WORKBOOK, page 55 — **2 Adjectives: Taste and Smell**

WORKBOOK PLUS, pages 85–86 — **2 Adjectives: Taste and Smell**

242 UNIT 7 Adjectives

4 **Incorporate** the information in the ***On Your Own*** notes for Students Acquiring English as part of your presentation of the grammar.
5 Use the **On Your Own** practice pages for Students Acquiring English before proceeding with the On Your Own activities in the pupil book.

Other Students Acquiring English notes in the Teacher's Edition

In addition to those notes that accompany the Meeting Individual Needs, Try It Out, and On Your Own sections, Students Acquiring English notes appear in several other places in each unit in the Teacher's Edition. The following chart shows the typical distribution of Students Acquiring English notes within the Teacher's Edition, though there are slight variations in the number and type of notes based on the number of pages in each Pupil Edition lesson.

- **Grammar, Usage, and Mechanics**
  Meeting Individual Needs
  Try It Out
  On Your Own
- **Getting Started**
- **The Writing Process**
- **Special Focus**
- **Assessment Link - Test Practice**

Students Acquiring English Test Practice notes and Blackline Masters

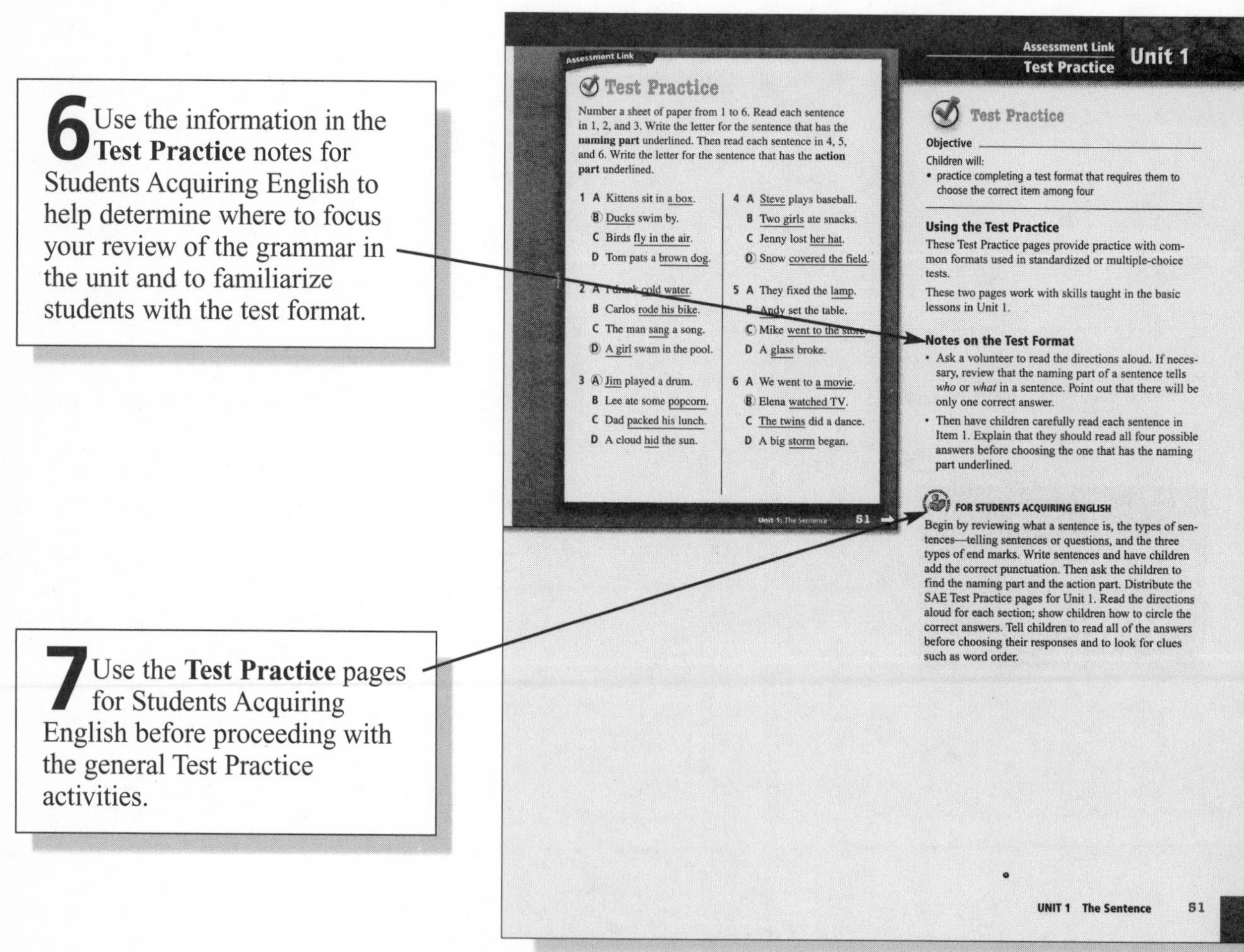

6 Use the information in the **Test Practice** notes for Students Acquiring English to help determine where to focus your review of the grammar in the unit and to familiarize students with the test format.

7 Use the **Test Practice** pages for Students Acquiring English before proceeding with the general Test Practice activities.

Assessment Link

Test Practice

Number a sheet of paper from 1 to 6. Read each sentence in 1, 2, and 3. Write the letter for the sentence that has the **naming part** underlined. Then read each sentence in 4, 5, and 6. Write the letter for the sentence that has the **action part** underlined.

1 A Kittens sit in a box.
(B) Ducks swim by.
C Birds fly in the air.
D Tom pats a brown dog.

2 A I drank cold water.
B Carlos rode his bike.
C The man sang a song.
(D) A girl swam in the pool.

3 (A) Jim played a drum.
B Lee ate some popcorn.
C Dad packed his lunch.
D A cloud hid the sun.

4 A Steve plays baseball.
B Two girls ate snacks.
C Jenny lost her hat.
(D) Snow covered the field.

5 A They fixed the lamp.
B Andy set the table.
(C) Mike went to the store.
D A glass broke.

6 A We went to a movie.
(B) Elena watched TV.
C The twins did a dance.
D A big storm began.

Unit 1: The Sentence 51

Assessment Link
Test Practice
Unit 1

Test Practice

Objective
Children will:
- practice completing a test format that requires them to choose the correct item among four

Using the Test Practice

These Test Practice pages provide practice with common formats used in standardized or multiple-choice tests.

These two pages work with skills taught in the basic lessons in Unit 1.

Notes on the Test Format

- Ask a volunteer to read the directions aloud. If necessary, review that the naming part of a sentence tells *who* or *what* in a sentence. Point out that there will be only one correct answer.
- Then have children carefully read each sentence in Item 1. Explain that they should read all four possible answers before choosing the one that has the naming part underlined.

FOR STUDENTS ACQUIRING ENGLISH

Begin by reviewing what a sentence is, the types of sentences—telling sentences or questions, and the three types of end marks. Write sentences and have children add the correct punctuation. Then ask the children to find the naming part and the action part. Distribute the SAE Test Practice pages for Unit 1. Read the directions aloud for each section; show children how to circle the correct answers. Tell children to read all of the answers before choosing their responses and to look for clues such as word order.

UNIT 1 The Sentence 51

Section 1

Using the Activity Masters

The Activity Masters in this section are specifically designed for use with **Beginning/Preproduction** and **Early Production/Speech Emergent** students. The Activity Masters are organized and grouped around basic themes and parts of speech and can be used to assess, teach, or review basic grammatical concepts. Their organization corresponds with the grammar units in *Houghton Mifflin English.*

Each blackline master is accompanied by teaching suggestions. Some of these suggestions have a strong oral emphasis; others concentrate on reading and writing. Use as many of these suggestions as time permits and select and recombine elements from various suggestions. Many of these suggestions refer to pair or group work, but they will work equally well if you or an aide are working with a student one-on-one.

Name ______________________________

1 Introductions

Practice this dialogue.

Hello. My name is ____________________.

What's your name?

My name is ____________________.

It's nice to meet you.

It's nice to meet you too.

Other Useful Expressions

Good morning. Good afternoon. Good evening.

How do you do? How are you?

Fine, thank you. I'm pleased to meet you.

Good-bye. So long. See you later. Good night.

More Questions and Answers

Where do you live?

I live ______________________________.

How old are you?

I'm ________________ years old.

Do you have any brothers and sisters?

I have __________ brothers and __________ sisters.

Do you play any sports?

Yes, I play ____________________. *or* No, I don't.

What do you like to do?

I like to ____________________.

MASTER

1 Introductions

Beginning/Preproduction

Suggestion #1

Present the dialogue with an English speaker, or have volunteers role-play. Point out appropriate body language and eye contact. Talk about use of first and last (family) names. Make sure students know where to insert their names. Then have partners practice the dialogue. Check for correct intonation and for pronunciation of contractions.

Suggestion #2

Work with the questions and statements; point out the question marks and periods. Have students repeat after you as you model falling intonation for *wh-* questions. Contrast this with the rising intonation of the questions with *Do*. Use hand motions to signal rising and falling intonation. Encourage students to make the motions with you.

Suggestion #3

Each student should have a pair of cards with a period and a question mark. Call out questions or statements from the master and have students raise the card that has the correct end mark. Call attention to the contrasting intonation of information questions and yes-no questions.

Suggestion #4

Dictate the Other Useful Expressions and have students write them. You may want to spell some of the more difficult words. Discuss possible answers to the questions in More Questions and Answers. Call attention to variations needed in "I have ____ brothers and ____ sisters" if one has one or no brothers and/or sisters and to the two possible answers for "Do you play any sports?"

Early Production/Speech Emergent

Suggestion #1

Have a pair of students role-play the dialogue. Ask volunteers to give the expanded forms of the contractions. Then have partners practice the dialogue. Check for correct intonation on the question and pronunciation of the contractions. Once students become comfortable with the initial dialogue, have partners proceed with More Questions and Answers.

Suggestion #2

Review or teach the Other Useful Expressions. Encourage students to insert the new expressions in the dialogue. Help students differentiate among *morning*, *afternoon*, *evening*. Explain that *So long* and *See you later* are informal.

Suggestion #3

Have students answer the questions in More Questions and Answers. Look for correct use of the preposition in the response to *Where do you live?* Note that the response can use *in*, *on*, or *at*. Interference from the first language will make these prepositions among the most challenging for students acquiring English. Call attention to and check for use of the infinitive verb in the response to *What do you like <u>to</u> do?*

Suggestion #4

Dictate the Other Useful Expressions and have students write them. Read each phrase twice, allowing ample time for students to write before repeating. Then have students check their work by reading the phrases aloud. Check spelling by asking the students to spell some of the more difficult words.

Name ____________________

2 Numbers

1	one
2	two
3	three
4	four
5	five
6	six
7	seven
8	eight
9	nine
10	ten
11	eleven
12	twelve
13	thirteen
14	fourteen
15	fifteen
16	sixteen
17	seventeen
18	eighteen
19	nineteen
20	twenty
21	twenty-one
22	twenty-two
23	twenty-three
24	twenty-four
25	twenty-five
26	twenty-six
27	twenty-seven
28	twenty-eight
29	twenty-nine
30	thirty
31	thirty-one
32	thirty-two
33	thirty-three
34	thirty-four
35	thirty-five
36	thirty-six
37	thirty-seven
38	thirty-eight
39	thirty-nine
40	forty

20	twenty
30	thirty
40	forty
50	fifty
60	sixty
70	seventy
80	eighty
90	ninety
100	one hundred
1,000	one thousand
10,000	ten thousand
100,000	one hundred thousand
1,000,000	one million

Phone Numbers

724-462-0138
503-899-4202
911
351-5000

Street Addresses

356 Donna Drive
4728 Whitman Road
8991 Green Street
222 Baker Avenue

MASTER

2 Numbers

Beginning/Preproduction

Suggestion #1

Read the numbers and have students repeat them after you. Help students distinguish between *thirteen/thirty*, *fourteen/forty*, and so on by emphasizing the difference in syllable stress between each set of two. Make sure students understand the pattern for the numbers 40 to 100. Write *hyphen* and *comma* on the board. Call attention to the hyphens in the words and the commas in the digits above 1,000. If students are ready, include a few additional examples above 100.

Suggestion #2

Model pronunciation of the numbers beginning with *th;* demonstrate the position of the tongue between the teeth. Read each number twice, allowing five to ten seconds between repetitions for students to look for and circle the number. Then call on students to dictate numbers for the group.

Suggestion #3

Go around the group, counting up to 100. Have each student give a number in turn. Listen for correct stress for contrasting pairs such as *thirteen/thirty*, *fourteen/forty*, and so on. Point out that regardless of the number, the words *hundred*, *thousand*, and *million* are all written and said as singular; i.e., *eight hundred*, not *eight hundreds*.

Suggestion #4

Students work in pairs. One student covers one of the columns of words, points to a digit, and asks the partner what the number is and how it is spelled.

Suggestion #5

Ask students to pay attention to the grouping of the numbers as you read first the phone numbers and then the addresses. Have students repeat after you. Explain that the number of digits in a phone number varies in other parts of the world and that these groupings differ in other languages. Ask students what their own phone number is. Help with number groupings.
Repeat with addresses.

Early Production/Speech Emergent

Suggestion #1

Point out the use of commas as opposed to decimal points. Explain that *hundred, thousand*, and *million* are written and said as singular regardless of the number; e.g., *37 million*, not *37 millions*. Have students read aloud the numbers. Write additional numbers for students to read aloud.

Suggestion #2

Call on volunteers to read the numbers and addresses. Call attention to the oral grouping of numbers we typically use for each. Then write several more phone numbers and street addresses on the board. Have students say the numbers along with you. Practice by asking the students to say their own phone numbers and street addresses.

Suggestion #3

Show students how the yellow pages are organized. Have them take turns reading phone numbers and addresses aloud. Then ask partners to find specific listings and ask each other about the phone number and address.

Name ________________________________

3 More Numbers

MASTER

3 More Numbers

Beginning/Preproduction

Suggestion #1

Have students write the digits for the numbers from 1 to 25 in order on the grid. Make sure students understand they should write in each row of the grid from top to bottom and from left to right. Have students demonstrate their understanding by tracing with their fingers the pattern they should follow. Later, have students take turns reading the numbers they wrote. Keep in mind that not all languages use the same digits as English.

Suggestion #2

Have students write the words for the numbers from 1 to 25 in the squares of the box instead of the digits. Remind students to use the hyphen. Later, correct the grid as a group, calling on students to spell out the words.

Suggestion #3

Fill in the words for most of the numbers from 1 to 25 on the grid, but leave several blank. Make copies of your grid and have students work individually or with partners to fill in the blanks. As an alternative, use even or odd numbers, again leaving several blanks.

Suggestion #4

Dictate random numbers for students to fill in the grid. Remember to note the numbers so that you don't forget what you called out. Have students work in small groups to check their work.

Early Production/Speech Emergent

Suggestion #1

Instruct students to write even numbers or odd numbers on the grid. Demonstrate what you mean by the terms *even* and *odd*. Later, partners check each other's work by saying the numbers to each other.

Suggestion #2

Dictate which numbers to write in which squares. For example: "Put number 6 in the first box. Write number 15 in the second square." Help students expand vocabulary by using alternatives such as *square* and *box*, *write* and *put*.

Suggestion #3

For practice following more complex directions, give instructions such as "Write number 25 in the center. Put 41 in the bottom left box." Review or teach direction words as needed. As an alternative, mix numbers and letters or numbers, letters, and shapes. For example, "Make a circle in the center. Put a 'b' in the bottom right box. Write number 14 in the next box to the left." Remember to work out your grid pattern ahead of time so that you don't forget what you called out.

Suggestion #4

Have students write the words for the numbers from 1 to 25 in the squares of the box instead of the digits. Remind students to use the hyphen where needed. Later, partners check each other's work by spelling the numbers to each other, or have students take turns spelling out words to correct the grid as a group.

Name ____________________

4 Days and Months

Days of the Week

Sunday	Wednesday	Saturday
Monday	Thursday	Sunday
Tuesday	Friday	

Months of the Year

January	May	September
February	June	October
March	July	November
April	August	December

Questions and Answers

What day is today?

Today is ____________________.

What day is tomorrow?

Tomorrow is ____________________.

What day was yesterday?

Yesterday was____________________.

Word Scramble

1. DYARIF ____________________
2. YAM ____________________
3. STUGASU ____________________
4. LUJY ____________________
5. STDAYEU ____________________
6. MNEVBREO ____________________
7. RRYAEBUF ____________________
8. AUYDNS ____________________

MASTER

4 Days and Months

Beginning/Preproduction

Suggestion #1

Read the names of the days of the week and have students repeat after you. Explain that we start the week with Sunday. Listen for correct pronunciation of the first syllable in *Thursday*. As needed, model the voiceless *th* and the voiced *s*. Next, chant the words and have students tap out the syllables with you. Continue with the months. Keep in mind that different calendars are used in other parts of the world.

Suggestion #2

Have students cut out the words for the days and the months. Have them sort the words into days and months. Then ask students to arrange each of the two sets of words in order. Remind them that we start the week with Sunday.

Suggestion #3

Present the question "What day is today?" Then proceed with "What day is tomorrow?" and "What day was yesterday?" Reinforce the words *today, tomorrow,* and *yesterday*. Ask students to find the verb in each question. Call attention to the past form.

Suggestion #4

Explain that in the Word Scramble the letters of the words are in the wrong order. Put *RLIPA* on the board and show students that these are the letters for *April*. Have students work individually or with partners to complete the activity.

Suggestion #5

Dictate the words for the days of the week and months of the year in random order. Say each word three times.

Early Production/Speech Emergent

Suggestion #1

Review or teach the days of the week and the months of the year. Present the pattern "March is the third month of the year." Review or teach *first* through *twelfth*. Then say a month and have students complete the sentence. For example: "December is the _____." Continue with questions such as "What is the fourth month of the year?"

Suggestion #2

Use the days of the week as a starting point for a discussion about routines. Ask students to describe their own weekly schedules. Prompt with questions such as "What do you do on Wednesday?" Check for appropriate use of the present tense in student responses.

Suggestion #3

Review or teach *today, tomorrow, yesterday*. Then have partners practice the questions and answers on the master. If students are ready, present *day after tomorrow* and *day before yesterday*.

Suggestion #4

Tell students to look at the lists of days and months as they complete the Word Scramble. After students complete the activity, have individuals or partners make their own. Remind students to count the number of letters and carefully check their puzzles. Students can then exchange Word Scrambles.

Activity Master

Name ___________________________

5 Calendar

MASTER

5 Calendar

Beginning/Preproduction

Suggestion #1

Have students make their own calendar for the current month, or have each student make a calendar of a different month. Provide actual reference calendars so that the first day of the month will be on the correct day of the week. Talk about things associated with each month and have the students decorate their calendars with drawings of objects such as colorful fall leaves or turkeys.

Suggestion #2

Explain that, in contrast to many languages, we use *first, second, third,* and so on to refer to the day of the month. Contrast ordinal numbers from *first* to *tenth* with the cardinal numbers one to ten. Present the ordinal numbers through *thirty-first*, but do not expect mastery. Reinforce the use of ordinals in dates by beginning each day's session with the day's date, saying, for example, "Today is September 25th."

Suggestion #3

Show students how to use a monthly calendar to make notes about school assignments or special events such as soccer games. Have students make a copy of the current month's calendar. Next, give them dates for things you have planned. Then ask them questions about their own activities. Guide the discussion with questions such as "What days do you play soccer?" "Does anyone in your family have a birthday this month?" Show students how to mark soccer for every Friday, for example. Students can use small drawings, or you can help them with words.

Early Production/Speech Emergent

Suggestion #1

Have each student make a calendar of a different month. Provide actual reference calendars so that the first day of the month will be on the correct day of the week. Talk about things associated with each month and have the students decorate their calendars with drawings of objects.

Suggestion #2

Explain that, in contrast to many languages, we use *first, second, third,* and so on to refer to the day of the month. Teach the ordinal numbers from *first* to *thirty-first* and contrast these with the cardinal numbers *one* to *thirty-one.* Reinforce the use of ordinals in dates by beginning each day's session with the day's date, saying, for example, "Today is September 25th" or by asking students for the date.

Suggestion #3

Ask students to make their own monthly calendars showing school assignments or special events such as soccer games. Provide them with dates for things you have planned. Remind them to include their own activities. Suggest that students use small drawings, words, or even their own abbreviations. Explain how to use personal abbreviations such as *soc.* for *soccer.*

Name ______________________________

6 Nouns: Animals

bird	cat	cow	goat	horse	monkey
mouse	sheep	dog	snake	turtle	frog

What Animal Is This?

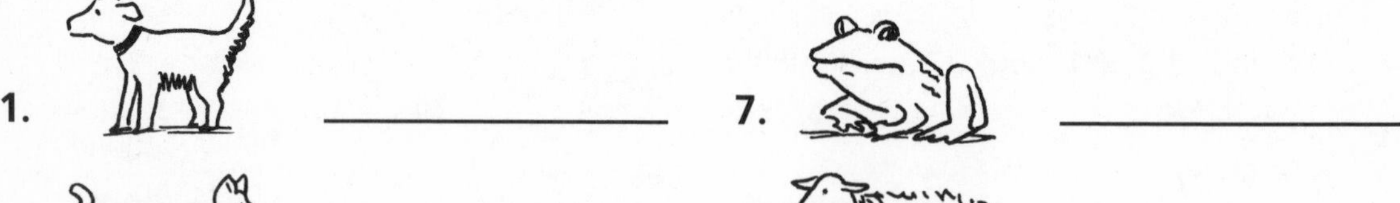

1. ____________ 7. ____________

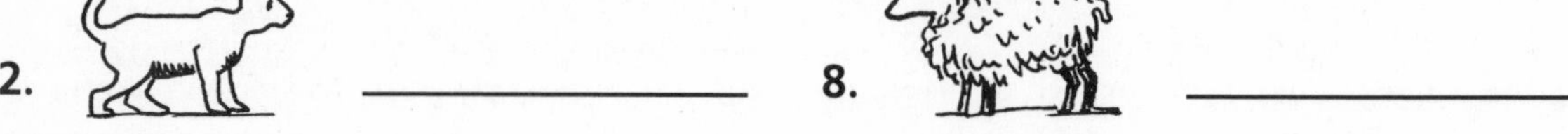

2. ____________ 8. ____________

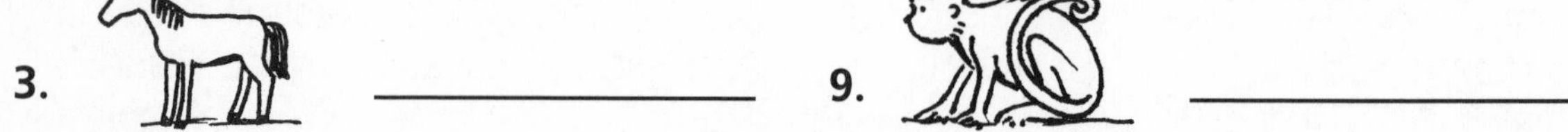

3. ____________ 9. ____________

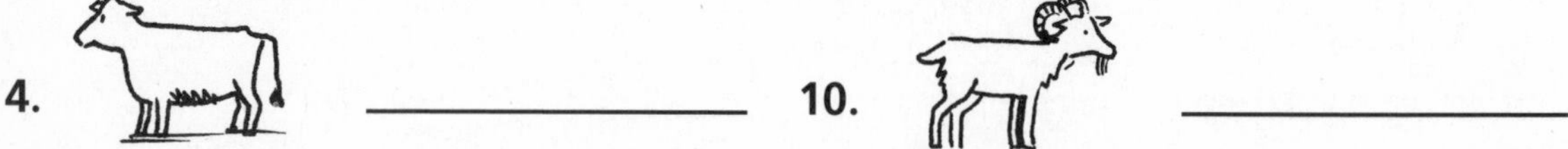

4. ____________ 10. ____________

5. ____________ 11. ____________

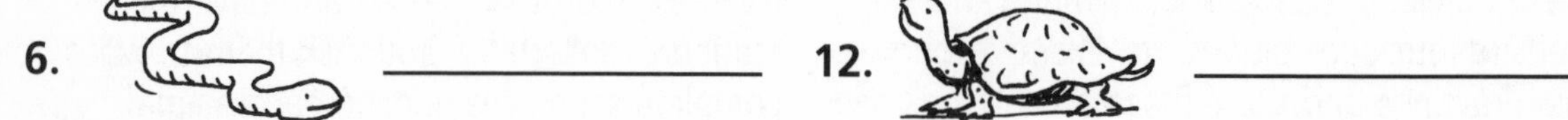

6. ____________ 12. ____________

Draw your favorite animal.

Name ______________________________

MASTER

6 Nouns: Animals

Beginning/Preproduction

Suggestion #1

Ask the question. Say the words in the box and have the students say them after you. Then point to each drawing and encourage volunteers to respond orally with the animal name. Help students write the name of each animal as a label. Emphasize that all of these drawings are nouns, naming words. Students then draw their favorite animals.

Suggestion #2

Read each word in the box and call on students to find the picture. Dictate the spelling of each animal name as students write it. Students draw and then name their favorite animals.

Suggestion #3

Ask the question. Call on individuals or the whole group in unison to respond with the complete sentence "It's a _____." Students write the complete sentence on another sheet of paper. Students draw their favorite animals and then write the name as a label.

Suggestion #4

Make duplicate sets of the drawings and use them to introduce plurals. For example, show two drawings and say: "These are horses" or "These are ducks." Have students repeat after you. Check for correct pronunciation of the plural endings, and make sure students are not using the article in the plural.

Suggestion #5

Use the animal cards to teach animal sounds in English. Encourage students to share the sounds the animals make in their home languages.

Early Production/Speech Emergent

Suggestion #1

Ask the question. Have each student respond with a complete sentence. Check for use of the article. Students draw and then label or write a sentence about their favorite animal. Emphasize that the animal names are nouns.

Suggestion #2

Point to a drawing and ask the question "Is this a _____?" Students then respond "Yes, it's a _____." or "No, it isn't a _____. It's a _____." Students should write their responses on another sheet of paper. Students draw and then talk about their favorite animals with a partner.

Suggestion #3

Brainstorm classifications for the animals. Write the classifications on the board and discuss what makes an animal *a mammal*, *a bird*, *a reptile*, or *an amphibian*. Students cut out the animals and sort them into these classifications.

Suggestion #4

Students complete the master with a partner. Read the words in the box and have the students repeat after you. Ask them to write complete sentences naming each animal. Remind students to use capital letters and a period at the end of each sentence. Then have partners take turns asking each other questions or describing the animals.

Name ____________________

7 Nouns: Classroom Objects

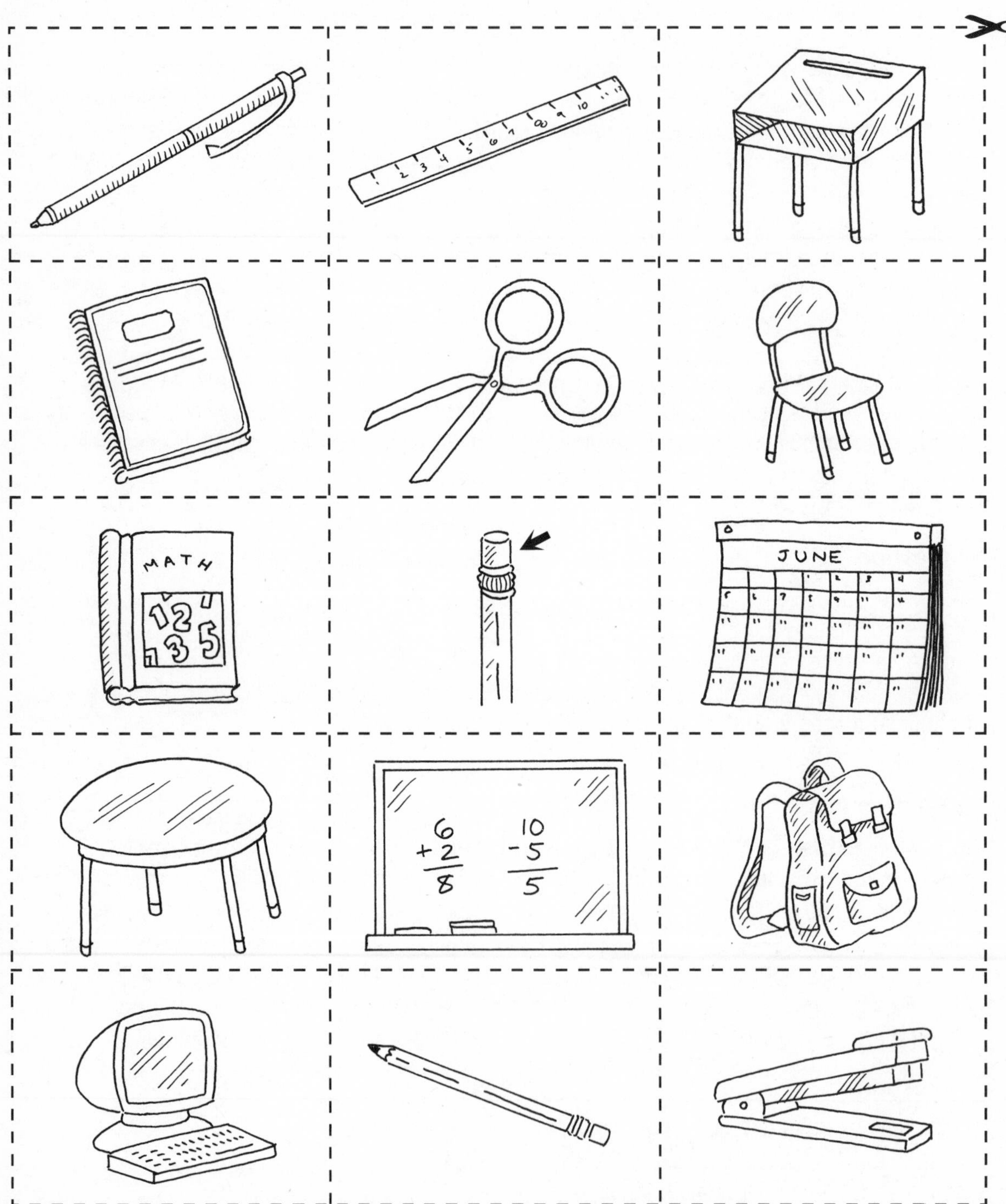

Name ____________________

8 Nouns: Classroom Objects

pen	ruler	desk
notebook	scissors	chair
textbook	pencil eraser	calendar
table	chalkboard	backpack
computer	pencil	stapler

MASTERS

7 & 8 Nouns: Classroom Objects

Beginning/Preproduction

Suggestion #1

Emphasize that the names of these drawings are nouns. Show students how to cut out the drawings of classroom objects on Master 7 and the words on Master 8 and make flashcards with the drawing on one side and the word on the other. Demonstrate how to use by holding up a card and asking the question "What's this?" Encourage students to respond in complete sentences. Point out that *scissors* is always plural. Check for use of the correct article.

Suggestion #2

Have the students cut out the drawings and the words for the objects and use them to play a matching game. Partners or teams with two players each place both sets of cards face down and look for the word that matches the drawing or vice versa. As players correctly match a drawing with its name, they remove the pair. The player or team with the most matched cards at the end wins.

Suggestion #3

Make duplicate sets of the drawings in Master 7. Use the drawings to introduce or practice plurals. For example, show two drawings and say: "These are pens" or "These are desks." Have students repeat after you. Check for correct pronunciation of the plural endings, and make sure students are not using the article in the plural.

Suggestion #4

Play Classroom TPR (Total Physical Response). Call on individuals to do various actions relating to classroom objects. For example, say: "Rita, stand next to the chalkboard" or "Alexander, go sit under the table." Show students how to make a check mark next to each word on Master 8 as you use it. Continue by allowing students to specify classmates and actions.

Early Production/Speech Emergent

Suggestion #1

Emphasize that the names of these drawings are nouns. Have students cut out the drawings and words and make flashcards. Have partners practice either by saying the word for the drawing or by reading the word and finding an example of that object in your classroom. Point out that *scissors* is always plural; check that students can read and pronounce the word correctly.

Suggestion #2

Use the drawings to teach or review plurals. Make duplicate sets of the drawings. Hold up two (or more) of the same noun and ask: "What are these?" Call on students to answer. Then have the group repeat the plural after you. Check for correct pronunciation of the plural endings. Make sure students are not using the article in the plural.

Suggestion #3

Choose one or more of the objects on Master 7. With students, brainstorm words to describe the chosen objects and list their ideas on a word web. Then ask partners to make their own word webs or to take turns describing other classroom objects. Circulate and assist with vocabulary as needed.

Masters 7 & 8 Nouns: Classroom Objects continued

Suggestion #4

Play classroom I Spy. Ask students to work as a group to find classroom objects for all of the words on Master 8. Students can cut out the words and then place the word card next to the classroom object. As an alternative, have teams secretly choose classroom objects and make notes about where each item is; then, using the clues, have another team figure out the objects they have selected. This version allows students to practice words and phrases for locations.

Name ______________________________

9 Nouns: Fruits and Vegetables

Name ______________________________

10 Nouns: Fruits and Vegetables

orange	potato	grapes
banana	tomato	lemon
strawberry	mushroom	pea pod
pear	apple	beans
pepper	peach	onion

MASTERS

9 & 10 Nouns: Fruits and Vegetables

Beginning/Preproduction

Suggestion #1

Emphasize that the names of these drawings are nouns. Have students cut out the drawings on Master 9 and the words on Master 10 and make flashcards with the drawing on one side and the word on the other. Hold up a card and ask the question "What's this?" Encourage students to respond in complete sentences such as: "It's an apple." Check for use of the correct article. Encourage the use of contractions in oral responses.

Suggestion #2

Have the students cut out the drawings and the words and use them for a matching game. Partners or teams of two players each place both sets of cards face down and look for the word that matches the drawing or vice versa. As players correctly match a drawing with its name, they remove the pair. The player who has the most matched cards at the end wins. You can also combine the set of cards for fruits and vegetables with the set for classroom objects in Masters 7 and 8.

Suggestion #3

Make duplicate sets of the drawings in Master 9. Use the drawings to practice plurals. For example, show two drawings and say: "These are oranges" or "These are onions." Have students repeat after you. Check for correct pronunciation of the plural endings, and make sure students are not using the article in the plural.

Suggestion #4

Use the drawings on Master 9 to work with colors. Have students color each piece of fruit or vegetable an appropriate color. Then call on volunteers to say which colors they have used. Encourage students to say if a fruit or vegetable could be more than one color.

Suggestion #5

Use Master 9. First, teach the words *fruit* and *vegetable*. Say that these are two important categories of food. Ask volunteers for examples of each type. Point out any of their examples that appear on Master 9. Then have students cut out the drawings and sort them into the two categories.

Early Production/Speech Emergent

Suggestion #1

Emphasize that the names of these drawings are nouns. Have students cut out the drawings and words and make flashcards. Have partners practice either by saying the word for the drawing or by reading the word and drawing the fruit or vegetable.

Suggestion #2

Use the drawings to practice or review plurals. Make duplicate sets of the drawings. Hold up two (or more) of the same noun and ask: "What are these?" Call on students to answer. Then have the group repeat the plural after you. Check for correct pronunciation of the plural endings. Also make sure students are not using the article in the plural.

Suggestion #3

Choose one of the fruits or vegetables on Master 9. With students, brainstorm words to describe that object and list their ideas on a word web. Then ask partners to make word webs or take turns describing other fruits and

Masters 9 & 10 Nouns: Fruits and Vegetables continued

vegetables on Master 9. Circulate and assist with vocabulary as needed.

Suggestion #4

Ask students about favorite and least liked foods. Prompt with questions such as "Who likes onions? Who doesn't like onions?" Have students raise their hands. Take a classroom poll of the responses; have all the students count and make their own notes of the results. Later, discuss what the poll showed.

Suggestion #5

Expand the lesson to include mass nouns for foods. Say that all the nouns on Master 9 can be counted. We can talk about *three apples* or *15 peas*, but there are other nouns in English that we cannot count. Explain that we do not say *breads*, *milks*, or *lettuces.* Instead we use quantifiers such as a *loaf of*, *a glass of*, and *a head of.* Explain that there are usually several different ways to quantify mass nouns. Present examples such as *a piece of candy* and *a pound of candy.* Encourage students to give other words for foods that they know and then try to determine which can be counted and which need mass nouns.

Name ____________________

11 Nouns: Parts of the Body

arm	foot	hair	hand
head	leg	neck	elbow

Name ______________________________

12 Nouns: Parts of the Body

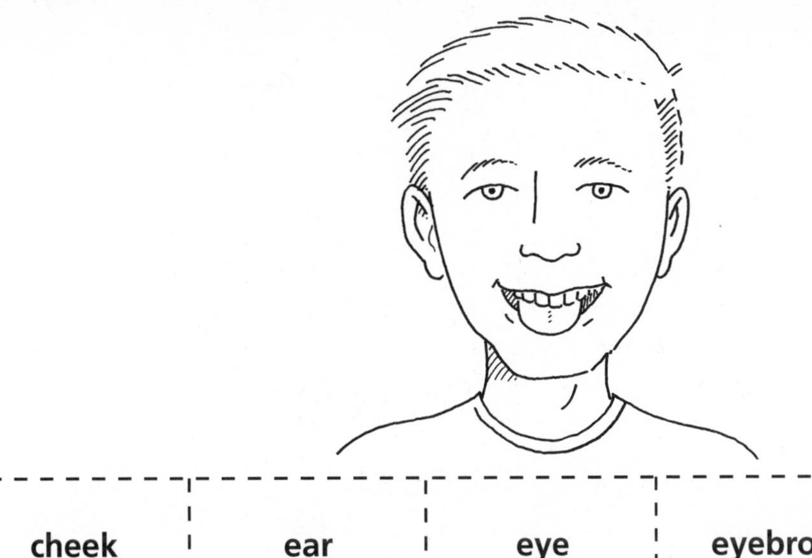

cheek	ear	eye	eyebrow	forehead
hair	mouth	nose	tooth	tongue

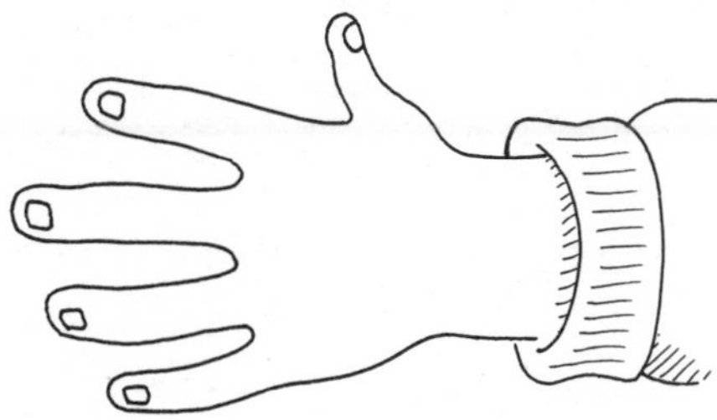

finger	fingernail	hand	thumb	wrist

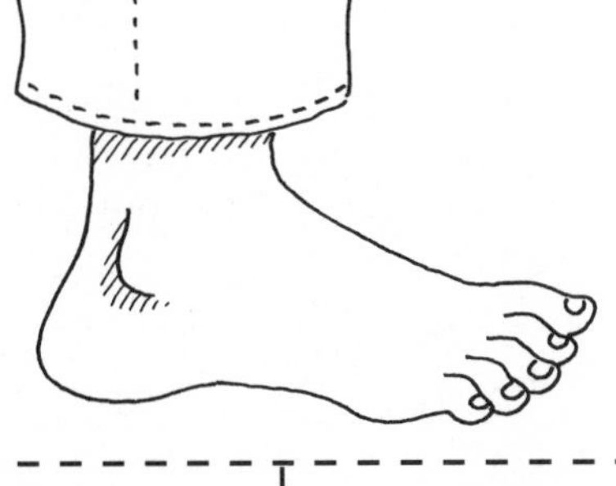

ankle	foot	toe	toenail

MASTERS 11 & 12 Nouns: Parts of the Body

Beginning/Preproduction

Suggestion #1

Emphasize that the names of the body parts are nouns. Teach the words *girl* and *boy*. Then teach *man* and *woman*. Next, read all the words for the body parts, pointing to yourself and then to the drawing. Say the words again and have students say the words as they point to their own bodies. Check for correct pronunciation of *tongue* and of the *th* in *thumb.* Also note that the *b* is silent. Point to the fingers and toes and explain that English has two different words.

Suggestion #2

Have students cut out the words for the body parts and paste them on the drawings in the appropriate spots. Students can work individually or with partners.

Suggestion #3

Play Simon Says. Show students how to play the game, demonstrating what to do in response to simple commands such as "Simon says touch your nose." You may also want to have the group act out all of the necessary verbs before you begin the game. These might include *touch*, *wiggle, wave, point to, bend.*

Suggestion #4

Ask yes-no and choice questions to help students learn groups of body parts. For example, ask: "Is the thumb a part of the foot or the hand? Does the woman have long hair?" Allow one- or two-word responses.

Early Production/Speech Emergent

Suggestion #1

Review or teach the words *boy, girl, man, woman.* Introduce the words for the body parts. Have students say the words with you. Then call out words for the body parts in random order. As you do so, students repeat the word and point to the spot on the drawing or on their own bodies.

Suggestion #2

Play Simon Says. First, ask if anyone has played Simon Says. Show students how to play the game by having those who know how to play respond to some simple commands such as "Simon says touch your ear." Have the group mime verbs *such as touch*, *wiggle, wave, point to,* and *bend* before you begin the game. Then call on different students to take a turn leading the game.

Suggestion #3

Have students make a list of ten words for body parts to dictate to a partner. Remind students to say the word twice, allowing several seconds for the partner to write the word before repeating it. Have students check their answers by spelling the words aloud.

Suggestion #4

Ask students questions to help them practice groups of body parts. For example, ask: "What are all the parts of the hand?" Accept simple oral lists as responses. For additional practice, have students write their answers. Allow students to refer to Masters 11 and 12 if needed.

Name ______________________________

13 Nouns: Clothing and Objects

Name ____________________

14 Nouns: Clothing and Objects

shirt	shoe	shorts	sock
cloud	book	tree	flowers

raincoat	umbrella	bus	taxi
puddle	wheel	boot	hat

boot	coat	glove	hat
sled	snow	trees	pants

MASTERS

13 & 14 Nouns: Clothing and Objects

Beginning/Preproduction

Suggestion #1

Emphasize that the names of the articles of clothing as well as the words for the objects are nouns. Have students cut out the words for the articles of clothing and the objects and paste them on the drawings in the appropriate spots.

Suggestion #2

Use the drawings on Master 13 to work with colors. Have students color each article of clothing or object. Then call on volunteers to say which colors they have used.

Suggestion #3

To prompt participation by all, ask for physical responses. For example: "Point to the umbrella." "Show me your shoes." "Show me how to button a shirt."

Suggestion #4

Play Funny Sentences. Write or say pairs of similar statements, one of which is nonsense, and ask students which sentence is okay. For example, write "I wear shorts in the winter" and "I wear boots in the winter" or "John wears shoes on his hands" and "John wears boots on his feet." For oral sentences, students can respond "Number 1" or "Number 2." Encourage students to draw one or two of their own funny sentences.

Early Production/Speech Emergent

Suggestion #1

Play Find the Mistake. Have partners cut out the words for the articles of clothing and the objects and place some in the right places and some in the wrong places on the drawings. Partners can use rubber cement for easy removal of the words. Then have another pair of students work with the master to correct the mistakes in labeling.

Suggestion #2

Use the drawings on Master 13 to practice colors. To begin, brainstorm a word web of colors. Do this on chart paper so that students can see the word and the color. Then have students color each article of clothing or object. Afterward, call on volunteers to say which colors they have used. Encourage students to begin to use words such as *light* and *dark* with the colors.

Suggestion #3

Ask yes-no, choice, and information questions about the drawings. For example: "Is the boy wearing a sunhat?" "Is the girl wearing shoes or sandals?" "Where's the umbrella?" "Where's the snow?" Continue with questions about students in the class. For example: "Is _____ wearing a red shirt or a blue sweater?"

Suggestion #4

Say the words for different articles and colors of clothing and have students locate a person wearing the same article of clothing in the classroom. Model the sentence stem "Tina is wearing _____." Include a few items that no one is wearing, such as a raincoat. Model the possible response, such as "No one is wearing a raincoat." Check for correct use of the article with singular nouns.

Name ______________________________

15 Nouns and Pronouns: Family

MASTER

15 Nouns and Pronouns: Family

Beginning/Preproduction

Suggestion #1

Say and write the words for all the family members on the board. Have students repeat after you as they point to each family member on Master 15. Later, have students cut out the family figures and paste them on poster board. You may want to have students draw a home setting. Help students label each figure. Have students invent sentences or a story about the figures.

Suggestion #2

Use the family figures to teach subject pronouns. Point to the mother and say *she*. Next, point to the sister and say *she*. Point to the two together and say *they*. Continue with the grandmother and then with the males. Practice by referring to people in the class, including yourself. To reinforce that *they* is used for all plurals, point out groups of mixed gender as well as groups of objects.

Suggestion #3

Have students cut out the family members on Master 15, paste them on another sheet, and label them with the correct word. Then ask students to draw their own families and add family member labels. Remind students to refer to their other paper to help them with the correct spelling of the words.

Early Production/Speech Emergent

Suggestion #1

Have students make a drawing of their own families with labels for each family member. Encourage students to include the individual's first name as well as the family relationship. Then have students talk about what they drew.

Suggestion #2

Use the family figures to teach or review subject pronouns. First, have students cut out the figures and group them under the pronouns *he* and *she*. Then ask students to say something about each family member beginning with either *She is* ____ or *He is* ____. For example, "She is the mother." Challenge students to say more than one sentence. For example: "This is the baby. She is one year old."

Suggestion #3

Use the family members to practice pronouns and professions. Have partners take turns introducing each family of figures. Provide a model such as the following: "This is the father. He is a teacher. This is the mother. She is a doctor." Listen for correct use of the articles and pronouns. You may want to take this opportunity to introduce or review vocabulary for professions. As an alternative, have students draw appropriate settings for each profession, cut out the figures, and place the figures in the scenes for the introductions.

Name ______________________________

16 Nouns: Rooms in a House

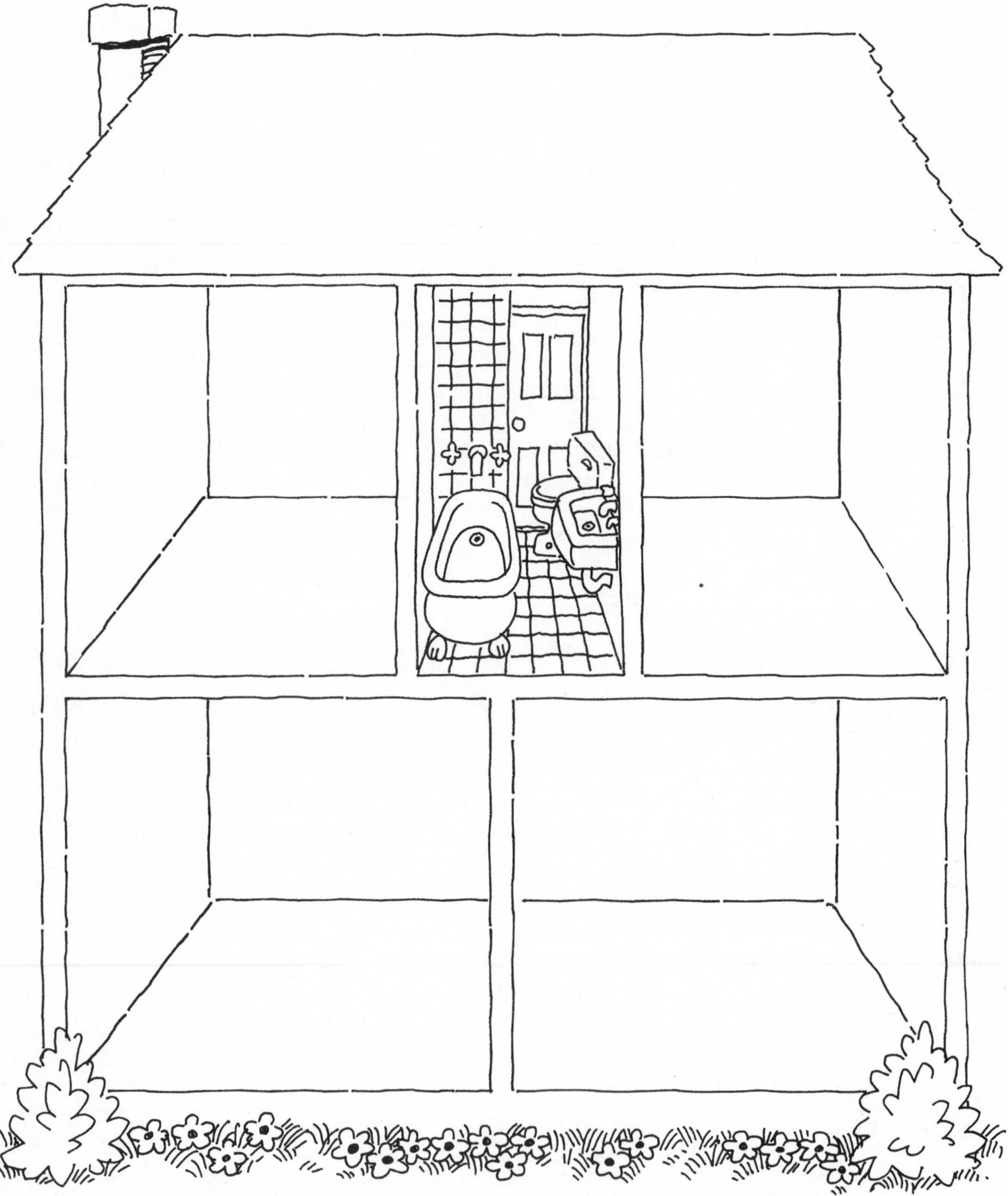

Name ______________________________

17 Nouns: Furniture

MASTERS

16 & 17 Nouns: Rooms in a House and Furniture

Beginning/Preproduction

Suggestion #1

Write and say the words *house* and *apartment* and have students repeat them after you. Next, introduce the words for the various rooms in a house or an apartment. Say each word as you point to the appropriate place on Master 16. Have students say the words after you and point to their own masters. Continue with the plumbing, appliances, and the furniture on Masters 16 and 17.

Suggestion #2

Say the words for various rooms and pieces of furniture and ask students to point to them. Then have students cut out the drawings of furniture on Master 17 and place them in appropriate rooms on Master 16. Later, ask questions to help students describe what they did. For example, ask: "Where did you put the bed?" Model responding with: "I put the bed in the bedroom."

Suggestion #3

Have students make drawings of their own houses or apartments. Help students write labels for the rooms. Challenge students to label some of the furniture as well.

Early Production/Speech Emergent

Suggestion #1

Say the words for the rooms and have students repeat the words and point to the rooms on their masters. Then dictate the words and have students write them on the drawing.

Suggestion #2

Have students make drawings of their own houses or apartments. Then have small groups work together to make labels for the rooms and furniture in their drawings. Encourage students to help each other with spelling.

Suggestion #3

Use Master 16. To practice sequence words and location, give students oral instructions about where to draw people and objects. Prepare a list of instructions in advance so that you can recall exactly what you said. For example, say: "First, draw the father by the stove in the kitchen. Next, draw the mother sitting at the table." Instruct students to make simple stick-figure drawings, but allow sufficient time for them to do so. As an alternative, write out your instructions and allow students time to prepare more detailed drawings.

Suggestion #4

Give students five minutes to label as many of the rooms and objects on Masters 16 and 17 as possible. Then have partners work together to check their work. Ask who has the most words written correctly.

Name ____________________

18 Noun Game

Name ______________________________

19 Noun Game

baby	frog	dog	peas	chicken
strawberry	chair	ear	shirt	notebook
duck	desk	backpack	sandal	mouth
bed	pencil	umbrella	nose	cow
eye	apple	stove	boot	

MASTERS

18 & 19 Noun Game

Beginning/Preproduction

Suggestion #1

Hold up Master 18 and ask students to find specific nouns. Say, for example: "Where's the apple?" "Point to the duck." Students can respond by pointing. Vary by pointing to the objects and asking questions such as: "Is this a duck or a chicken?" "What's this?"

Suggestion #2

Cut out a sufficient number of the 24 pieces of art and 24 words on Masters 18 and 19 so that each student will have one square. Make sure to use only art and words that will match. Students circulate, looking for the person who has the match for his or her word or piece of art. Have students stand together with the person who has the match. When all the students have found their matches, ask: "Who has the eyes?" at which point that pair raises their hands.

Suggestion #3

Using only Master 18, have partners or small groups work together to write the words for as many of the objects on the page as possible. Students can write the word for each item as a label. Then pass out Master 19 and have them check their work. Ask them to correct any misspelled words.

Suggestion #4

Play Concentration. Cut out the pieces of art and words on Masters 18 and 19 and distribute a total of 10 or 12 squares to each pair or team. Make sure the squares you distribute will all form matches. Students place all of the squares face down and turn them up two at a time looking for matches. As a match is made, the player takes the two cards and removes them from the table. The player or team with the most matches at the end wins.

Suggestion #5

Check vocabulary and comprehension by having students make their own drawings for the words on Master 19. Students can work in small groups with each person completing drawings for one row of words.

Early Production/Speech Emergent

Suggestion #1

Call on students to identify each piece of art on Master 18. Point to each piece of art and ask: "What's this?" Encourage students to respond with a full sentence and contractions, as in "It's a strawberry." Check for correct use of the indefinite article.

Suggestion #2

Cut out a sufficient number of the 24 pieces of art and words on Masters 18 and 19 so that each student will have one or two squares, depending on the total number of students. Students circulate, looking for the person who has the match for his or her word or piece of art. Model the questions: "Do you have the _____?" "Do you have the word _____?" After all the students have found their matches, ask individuals: "What do you have?" "Who has the _____?" to which the student responds: "I have the _____." "_____ has the _____."

Masters 18 & 19 Noun Game continued

Suggestion #3

Have students work in pairs. Student A uses Master 18 and student B uses Master 19. They alternate asking each other questions about objects and words on the two pages. Student B might ask: "Where's the umbrella?" Student A points to the drawing or says, for example: "The umbrella is next to the backpack." Student A might say: "Where is the word *mouth?*"

Suggestion #4

Play Concentration. Cut out the pieces of art and words on Masters 18 and 19 and distribute a total of 24 squares to each pair or team. Make sure the squares you distribute will all form matches. Students place all of the squares face down and turn them up two at a time looking for matches. As a match is made, the player takes the two cards and removes them from the table. The player or team with the most matches at the end wins.

Suggestion #5

Use duplicate sets of Master 18 to review or teach plurals. Cut out the squares and hold up the two drawings of the baby, for example. Ask: "What are these?" Students respond "They're babies." This activity can be done orally or in writing.

Name ______________________________

20 Verbs: Actions

Name ______________________________

21 Verbs: Actions

MASTERS

20 & 21 Verbs: Actions

Beginning/Preproduction

Suggestion #1

Say that all of the places and things on Master 20 are associated with actions; these actions are called verbs. Call on volunteers to suggest actions associated with the places and things shown on Master 20. Any verb that fits the art is acceptable, whether regular or irregular.

Suggestion #2

Use Master 20 to practice simple present with *you* and *I*. Ask students yes-no questions about their own activities. For example, point to number 1 and ask: "Do you swim every day?" If needed, model the responses "Yes, I swim every day" or "No, I don't swim every day." Some students may be familiar with the short forms "Yes, I do" and "No, I don't."

Suggestion #3

Use Master 20 and Master 21 together to work with third person singular and plural subjects and verbs. Ask students what pronoun they can use for each piece of art on Master 21. Use the first one as an example with *he*. Then show students how to combine the art on the two masters to make a sentence such as "He swims every day."

Suggestion #4

Use Masters 20 and 21 to work on other verb tenses. Questions about the future can be answered easily because no irregular forms are needed. "Will you swim tomorrow?" can be answered as "Yes, I will swim tomorrow" or "Yes, I will." A negative response allows you to introduce *won't*. Questions about the past such as "Did you swim yesterday?" will allow you to introduce some common irregular forms.

Early Production/Speech Emergent

Suggestion #1

Say that all of the places and things on Master 20 are associated with actions; these actions are called verbs. Have partners work together to think of possible actions associated with the places and things shown on Master 20. Then list students' ideas for each action on the board. Verbs might include: *swim, run, play (soccer), sing, ride* or *go, talk or call, eat, wash* or *brush (teeth), read* or *study*. Any verb that fits the art is acceptable, whether regular or irregular.

Suggestion #2

Use Master 20 to practice simple present with *you* and *I*. Ask students yes-no questions about their own activities. For example, point to number 1 and ask a student: "Do you swim every day?" Students may respond with long or short answers.

Suggestion #3

Use Master 20 and Master 21 together to work with third person singular and plural subjects and verbs. Show students how to combine the art on the two masters to make a sentence such as "He swims every day." Have students work with partners to make sentences for each pair of drawings. Encourage students to be creative with their sentences. Afterward, ask students to share their sentences.

Name ______________________________

22 Verbs: More Actions

Name ____________________

23 Verbs: More Actions

kick	run	wave
write	walk	laugh
sleep	jump	fly
cry	look	read
sing	eat	study

MASTERS 22 & 23 Verbs: More Actions

Beginning/Preproduction

Suggestion #1

Call on volunteers to identify the actions shown on Master 22; list students' ideas on the board. Remind students that the words are verbs. Make suggestions when necessary. Any verb that fits the art is acceptable, whether regular or irregular. Then have students compare their ideas with the verbs shown on Master 23.

Suggestion #2

Use Master 22 to work with third person singular subjects and verbs. Use the first one as an example with *she*. Say: "She kicks the ball." Work with students as a group to continue the activity.

Suggestion #3

Use Masters 22 and 23 to work on other verb tenses. Questions about the future can be answered easily because no irregular forms are needed. For example, "Will you read the book?" can be answered as "Yes, I will read the book" or "Yes, I will." A negative response allows you to introduce the contraction *won't*. Questions about the past such as "Did you read the book yesterday?" will allow you to introduce some additional common irregular forms.

Suggestion #4

Use Master 23. Have the students demonstrate understanding of written or spoken words by acting out the verbs. Call on a student. Then point to or say a word. The student acts out the verb. If the person is correct, he or she chooses the next verb.

Early Production/Speech Emergent

Suggestion #1

Have partners identify the actions shown on Master 22; list students' ideas on the board. Remind students that the words are verbs. Make suggestions in cases where students are unable to do so. Any verb that fits the art is acceptable, whether regular or irregular. Then have students compare their ideas with the verbs shown on Master 23.

Suggestion #2

Use Master 22 to work with third person singular subjects and verbs. Have students work with partners to make sentences for each verb and drawing. Encourage students to be creative with their sentences.

Suggestion #3

Point to a piece of art on Master 22. Prompt students to use specific tenses with time words such as *yesterday, tomorrow, now,* and *always* and ask them to make a statement about the art. For example, pointing to the man singing, say: "Yesterday." The student responds "Yesterday the man sang" or "Yesterday the man was singing." Make sure students understand that *always*–which expresses frequency–appears just before the verb, but time words like *yesterday, tomorrow,* and *now* can appear at the beginning or end of the sentence.

Suggestion #4

Play TPR Commands, using the verbs on Master 23. Have students perform two actions. For example: "First jump on one foot. Then wave at me." Allow students to have a turn choosing the actions.

Name ____________________

24 Describing a Park Scene

Name ______________________________

25 Describing a Beach Scene

MASTERS

24 & 25 Describing Park and Beach Scenes

Beginning/Preproduction

Suggestion #1

Ask students a variety of questions about people, objects, and actions. For example, for Master 24 say: "Point to a dog. Are the girl and boy playing baseball or soccer? Is the man sleeping or eating? Who is riding a bicycle?" For Master 25, say: "Count the birds. Are there two or three birds?"

Suggestion #2

Use the art to practice the present progressive. Introduce the tense by performing several actions and saying what you are doing. For example, as you perform the action, say: "I'm walking to the door. I'm opening the door. Maria is looking at me." Make sure students understand that the helping verb will be *is* or *are* and the main verb will be in the *-ing* form. Emphasize that the action is taking place now. Point to the master and give one or two examples. Then ask: "What is _____ doing? What are _____ doing?" Listen for the correct verb form. Assist with vocabulary as needed.

Suggestion #3

Assign students to two teams. Have each team work with a different master. Ask the teams to name five verbs in each drawing. Each of five team members will act out one of the verbs while the other team guesses what the verb is. As soon as the opposing team guesses, the teams change turns. If the opposing team cannot guess, the team presenting gets a point.

Suggestion #4

Prepare a list of objects, people, or actions for students to find on each of the two masters. Have students circle the items they find on your list. Later, as the group checks the answers, ask students which words are nouns and which are verbs.

Suggestion #5

Use the masters to practice spelling. For example, say to individual students: "Find a K-I-T-E. Point to the D-O-G. Where is the B-A-B-Y?"

Suggestion #6

Have students make their own drawings of a park or a beach. Help them make labels for the people, objects, and actions.

Early Production/Speech Emergent

Suggestion #1

Ask students a variety of questions about people, objects, and actions. For example, for Master 24 ask: "What are the girl and boy doing? Where is the man sleeping? What place is this?" For Master 25, ask: "How many birds are there? How many people do you see?"

Suggestion #2

To practice past tense forms of verbs, ask students about their own visits to a beach or a park. Guide the students with questions such as: "Have you been to the beach? When did you go? Did you have a good time? What did you do there?" Help students with past tense forms of verbs. If students seem ready, encourage them to write two or three sentences describing their time at the beach or a park.

Masters 24 & 25 Describing Park and Beach Scenes continued

Suggestion #3

Have partners work together to plan a list of five questions to ask another pair of students. The questions can be done orally or in writing.

Suggestion #4

Have students make their own drawings of a park or a beach. Ask them to make labels for the people, objects, and actions. Assist with vocabulary. Then ask students to describe their drawings for the group.

Name ______________________________

26 Adjectives: Opposites

MASTER

26 Adjectives: Opposites

Beginning/Preproduction

Suggestion #1

Introduce adjectives for each of the drawings on Master 26. Possibilities include: *tall/short, black/white, clean/dirty, old/new, cloudy/sunny, expensive/cheap or expensive/inexpensive, long/short, big/little* or *big/small, healthy/sick or healthy/unhealthy, hot/cold, dry/wet, and good/bad or delicious/terrible.* Emphasize that these are describing words. Model adjectives in context phrases or sentences so that students can become familiar with the position in relation to the noun.

Suggestion #2

Students cut out the pictures, paste them on another sheet, then write the two adjectives under each drawing. You may want to dictate the words, spelling any that are problematic.

Suggestion #3

Ask students if they can think of any other describing words. Make a list of their ideas. Prompt them by pointing out that colors and numbers are describing words.

Suggestion #4

Use the drawings to introduce *this* and *that* and comparisons. Point to the drawing and say, for example: "This man is taller than that man," "This pencil is longer than that pencil," or "This ring is more expensive that that ring." Call attention to the *-er* with one- or two-syllable words, *more* with longer words, and the word *than*. Have students tap out the syllables with you.

Early Production/Speech Emergent

Suggestion #1

Have students identify the opposites. Possibilities include: *tall/short, black/white, clean/dirty, old/new, cloudy/sunny, expensive/cheap* or *expensive/inexpensive, long/short, big/little* or *big/small, healthy/sick* or *healthy/unhealthy, hot/cold, dry/wet,* and *good/bad or delicious/terrible*. Contrast *long/short* and *tall/short*, saying that something that is upright, such as a person, a tree, or a building can be tall.

Suggestion #2

Introduce comparisons. Point to the drawing and say: "This man is taller than that man," or "This ring is more expensive that that ring." Call attention to the *-er* with one- or two-syllable words, *more* with longer words, and the word *than*. Have students tap out the syllables with you. Present additional words, again having students tap out the syllables to help determine the ending. Then ask students for other describing words. Continue choosing the comparative form by tapping out syllables.

Suggestion #3

Say an adjective from Master 26 and have students call out or write its opposite. For practice with adjective position, call out an adjective and have students use it in a sentence. This can be done orally or in writing.

Suggestion #4

Ask small groups to make a word web of describing words for an object in the classroom. Model a word web of describing words for an object such as a desk.

Name ______________________________

27 Adjectives: Contrasting

MASTER
27 Adjectives: Contrasting

Beginning/Preproduction

Suggestion #1

Point to one of the people or objects in each set of three on Master 27. Model the use of adjectives by describing the person or object. Then make a comparison among the three. Have students repeat after you. Several adjectives may be used to describe the drawings on Master 27. These include: *high/low* or *tall*, *tall* or *short*, *clean* or *dirty*, *old* or *new*, *light* or *heavy*, *hot* or *cold*. Introduce comparatives and superlatives using Master 27.

Suggestion #2

For additional practice with comparatives and superlatives, gather groups of three students or sets of three classroom objects. Help students tap out syllables to determine whether *-er/-est* or *more/most* is needed.

Suggestion #3

For more practice with adjectives, help students describe people and objects in the classroom. You may want to teach categories such as colors, shapes, feelings, or tastes. Be sure students understand that numbers are also adjectives.

Early Production/Speech Emergent

Suggestion #1

Have partners think of adjectives they could use to describe the people and objects in the drawings on Master 27. Several adjectives may be used to describe these drawings. They include: *high/low* or *tall*, *tall* or *short*, *clean* or *dirty*, *old* or *new*, *light* or *heavy*, *hot* or *cold*. Afterward, ask students to share their ideas with the group. Introduce comparatives and superlatives using Master 27.

Suggestion #2

For additional practice, have students think of ways to describe groups of three people or three classroom objects. Suggest that students tap out syllables to determine whether *-er/-est* or *more/most* is needed.

Suggestion #3

Provide magazines for students to cut up and prepare their own sets of three people or objects for comparison. With students, brainstorm some of the adjectives they might use for this activity.

Name ______________________________

28 Adverbs: When, Where, How

When?

always usually often sometimes never
today tomorrow yesterday soon now

Where?

downtown inside outside upstairs
downstairs everywhere there

How?

easily carefully quickly loudly
angrily happily badly

Word Scramble

1. NOOS ______________________
2. HTREE ______________________
3. YLDAB ______________________
4. VREEN ______________________
5. SLIYEA ______________________
6. NNWWOOTD ______________________

MASTER

28 Adverbs: When, Where, How

Beginning/Preproduction

Suggestion #1

Use Master 28 to introduce the concept of adverbs. Say that adverbs are the describing words we use for verbs. Demonstrate by walking slowly, talking loudly, and singing softly. Introduce *slowly, loudly, softly*. Say the words and have students repeat them after you. Write the words and say them again. Point to the *-ly* ending. Work separately with the categories of words under *When?*, *Where?*, and then *How?* Then do the Word Scramble as a group.

Suggestion #2

Use adverbs on Master 28 as you ask students yes-no and choice questions about their own activities. As you ask the question, point to the word you have used. For example, ask: "Do you usually ride the bus, or do you always ride the bus?" "Do you like to go downtown?" Try to incorporate adverbs in your speaking in order to emphasize their placement in the sentence.

Early Production/Speech Emergent

Suggestion #1

Use Master 28 to introduce the concept of adverbs. Make the analogy with the describing words we call adjectives, saying that adverbs are the describing words we use for verbs. Demonstrate by walking slowly, talking loudly, and singing softly. Write and say *slowly, loudly, softly.* Have students repeat after you. Call attention to the *-ly* ending. Ask if students know any other words that end this way. Work with the categories of words under *When?*, *Where?*, and then *How?* Then have students do the Word Scramble individually or with a partner.

Suggestion #2

Use adverbs on Master 28 as you ask students a variety of questions about their own activities. As you ask the question, point to the word you have used. For example, ask: "What time do you usually get up?" "Do you usually eat dinner at 5:00, or do you always eat dinner at 5:00?" "Do you like to go downtown?" Point out that *always, usually, often, sometimes,* and *never* form a series from 100% to 0%.

Suggestion #3

Have partners make their own Word Scrambles, using the words on Master 28. Remind students to check their work *carefully* by counting letters. Then have partners exchange papers and solve the scrambles.

Name ______________________________

29 Adverbs: Negatives

ever	anyone	anywhere	none	nothing
any	anything	never	no one	nowhere

Questions and Negative Answers

Did anyone call?

No, no one called.

Did anyone come?

No, ______________________.

Did you lose anything?

No, I didn't lose anything.

Did you find anything?

No, ______________________.

Have you ever been to London?

No, I have never been to London.

Have you ever seen a tiger?

No, ______________________.

MASTER

29 Adverbs: Negatives

Beginning/Preproduction

Suggestion #1

Explain that a negative is like saying "no." Give the example: "I don't have any pencils." "I have no pencils." Say that these two sentences mean the same but the grammar of the sentence is different. Present a question with *any* and say that the non-negative word is the one we use for a question. Now refer to the pairs on Master 29. Have students cut out the words and make a pile. Then have students work in small groups to put the words into negative and non-negative groups. Finally, have students match up each negative word with the right non-negative word.

Suggestion #2

Have students cut out the words from Master 29. Ask the students to pair each negative word with a non-negative word. Then select some pairs and help students create a sentence for each word in a pair. Write the sentences on the board. Have a student come up and underline the adverb in each one.

Suggestion #3

Read the questions and have students give the answers in the first column on Master 29 chorally. Then ask the questions in the second column and ask the students to respond again chorally.

Early Production/Speech Emergent

Suggestion #1

Have students cut out the words from Master 29 and make a single pile. Then ask the students to put the cards into negative and non-negative groups. Next, ask them to match up each negative word with its non-negative word. Finally, partners or small groups write two sentences for each card. Ask students to underline the adverb in each one. Make sure students understand that the non-negative word is the one we use for a question.

Suggestion #2

Read the questions and call on students to give the answers in the first column on Master 29. Then ask the questions in the second column and ask the students to respond.

Suggestion #3

Have students draw a card from the pile and give a sentence orally using that adverb. Remind students that they may use the non-negative words to make statements or questions. Emphasize that the negatives are used for statements only.

Name ______________________________

30 Prepositions: Location

MASTER

30 Prepositions: Location

Beginning/Preproduction

Suggestion #1

Use examples and the master to introduce the concept of preposition, explaining that these words often tell about location. Then ask students yes-no and choice questions about the drawings on Master 30. Keep in mind that choice of prepositions varies considerably among languages and that *in, on, at,* though among the most common prepositions, are the most problematic. For example, ask: "Is the cat on the table or under the table?" As you ask the question, use gestures to indicate the meaning of the preposition.

Suggestion #2

Have students cut out the drawings on Master 30 and put them face down in a pile. Have each student draw a card and describe the position of the person, animal, or object.

Suggestion #3

Have each student take a turn placing an object in a different place in the room. The rest of the group must then describe where that object was and where it is now.

Early Production/Speech Emergent

Suggestion #1

Use examples and the master to introduce the concept of preposition. Explain that these words often tell about location. Ask students a variety of questions about the drawings on Master 30. Call attention to the fact that *in, on, at,* though among the most common prepositions in English, are the ones that are most likely to differ from the students' first languages. For example, ask: "Where is the cat?" If needed, use gestures to indicate the meaning of the preposition.

Suggestion #2

Have students cut out the drawings on Master 30 and put them face down in a pile. Have each student draw a card and ask a question about the position of the person, animal, or object. The question can ask for a yes-no, choice, or information response. The next student responds and then chooses a card to ask a question.

Suggestion #3

Discuss prepositions and modes of transportation. Explain that in English if we are able to stand up, we usually say *on.* Refer to the drawings on Master 30. Then refer to other modes of transportation such as a taxi, boat or ship, or helicopter and have students say whether we would say *on* or *in.*

Name ______________________________

31 Prepositions: Find the Mistakes

MASTER

31 Prepositions: Find the Mistakes

Beginning/Preproduction

Suggestion #1

Ask students a variety of questions about people, objects, and actions on Master 31. For example, say: "Point to the frog. Where is the frog?" Remind students that prepositions often tell about location.

Suggestion #2

Prepare a list of things for students to find on Master 31. Have students circle the items on your list. Later, as a group, check the answers.

Suggestion #3

Have partners or teams move objects around in the classroom so that they are in the wrong place. Students can put their heads down and cover their eyes, or a team can make the changes while the rest of the group is at recess or at lunch. Then have students find the mistakes. Help students describe what they found and where the object normally should be.

Early Production/Speech Emergent

Suggestion #1

Introduce the concept of preposition, explaining that these words often tell about location. Referring to Master 31, have students describe the location of people and objects. Encourage students to use complete sentences. Write the sentences on the board, or have volunteers do so.

Suggestion #2

Assign students to two teams. Ask the teams to find five things wrong in the drawing. Each of five team members will then act out what they find. As soon as the opposing team guesses, the teams change turns. If the opposing team cannot guess, the team presenting gets a point.

Suggestion #3

Have students make their own drawings of a place where things are not where they should be. Then have students exchange drawings and find the mistakes. Help students describe what they found wrong and where the object normally would be.

Section 2

The Activity Masters in this section are specifically designed for use with students who are at the **Intermediate and Advanced stages of English proficiency.** They correspond to the organization of the grammar units in the pupil books of *Houghton Mifflin English.* There are *two* masters for every grammar lesson; one page accompanies the *Try It Out* exercise in the pupil book; the other page accompanies the *On Your Own* activity.

Table of Contents

(*Table of Contents* continued)

Unit 6 Pronouns

Name

LESSON
1 What Is a Sentence?

Part 1

Use the words in the box to label the parts of the dog.

Part 2

Write *sentence* or *not* for each group of words.

Example: Buddy has big ears. sentence

1. Buddy my dog. ____________
2. Buddy jumps. ____________
3. The dog big.____________
4. The dog is black and white. ____________
5. He is playing. ____________
6. He running. ____________

Name ______________________________

LESSON

1 What Is a Sentence?

Complete the sentences about the beaver. Fill in the blanks with a word that tells who or what, or a word that tells what happens. There may be more than one possible answer.

Example: The beaver ____swims____ in the water.

1. The beaver ________________ a flat tail.
2. The ________________ looks like a paddle.
3. The beaver ________________ strong teeth.
4. The beaver's ________________ is soft.
5. The beaver ________________ its house in the water.
6. The beaver ________________ hard.

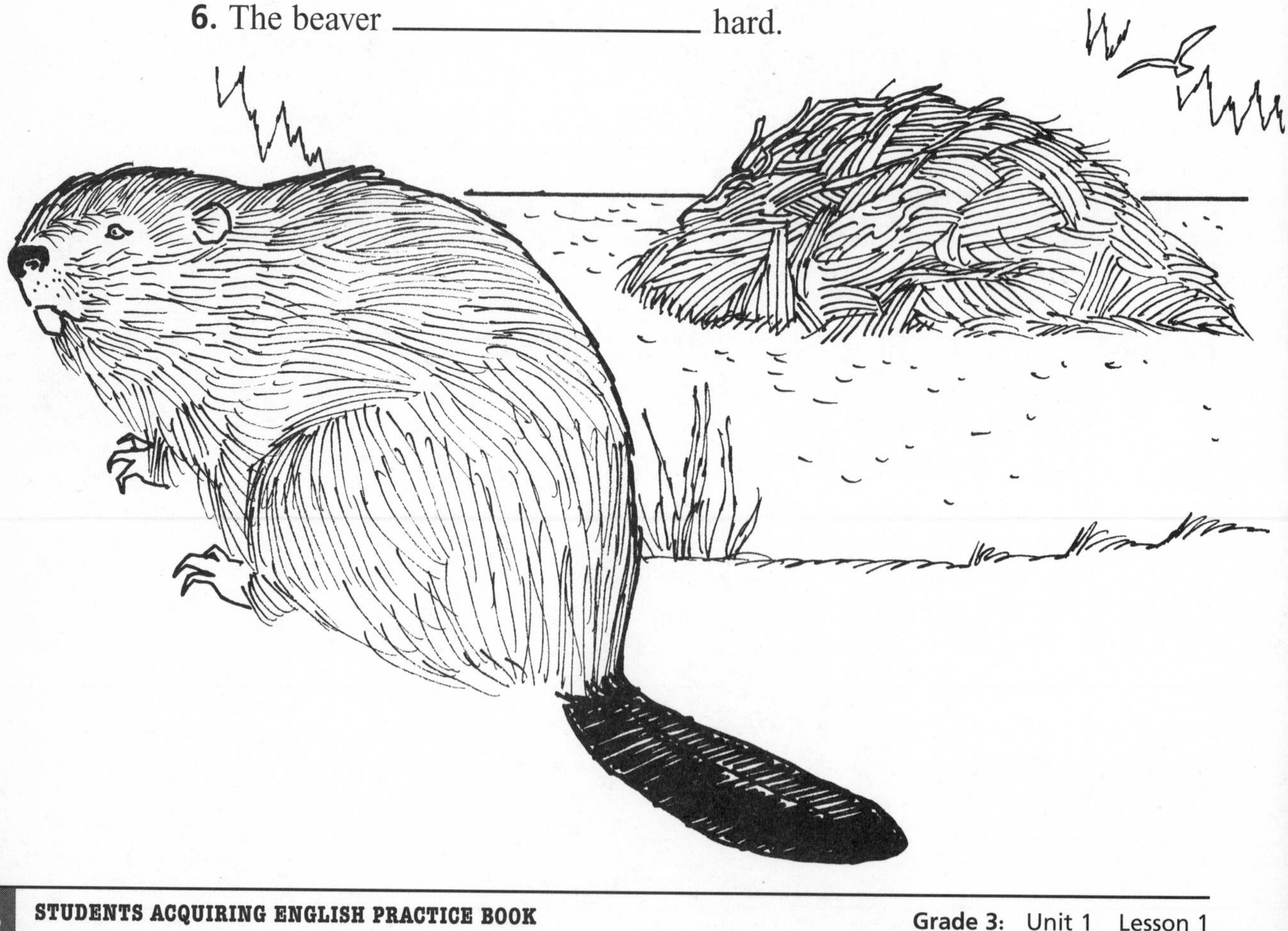

Name ______________________________

LESSON

2 Statements and Questions

Is each sentence a statement or a question? Write *S* for a statement. Write *Q* for a question.

Example: This is my family. __S__

1. What is your name? _____

2. I'm from Guatemala. _____

3. My family came to the United States last year. _____

4. Do you speak Spanish? _____

5. Yes, I do. _____

6. Where do you live? _____

7. I live on First Street. _____

8. How old are you? _____

Name ______________________________

LESSON
2 Statements and Questions

ON YOUR OWN

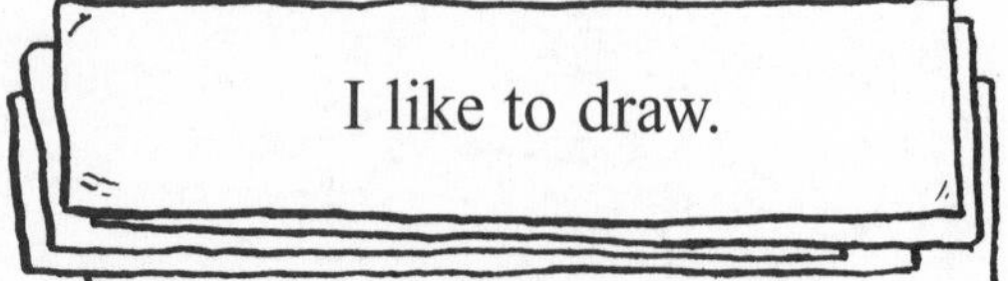
I like to draw.

Do you have any pets?

Cut up the sentence strips below. Then put the sentence strips into two piles. Make one pile for statements and one pile for questions.

1. How old are you?
2. His name is James.
3. I am in third grade.
4. Who is your best friend?
5. I have two brothers.
6. Who is your favorite teacher?
7. I like to play soccer.
8. Do you like pizza?
9. Where are my books?
10. The girls are talking.
11. Is this your bike?
12. My friend is in third grade too.

Name ______________________________

LESSON

3 Commands and Exclamations

Is each sentence a command or an exclamation? Write *C* for a command. Write *E* for an exclamation.

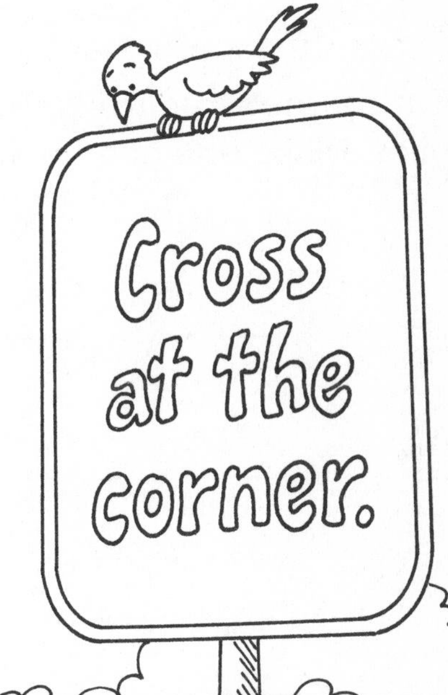

Example: Pick up your clothes. C

1. Sit down, please. ______
2. I dropped my ice cream! ______
3. Spell his name for me. ______
4. I can't find my English book! ______
5. Wait for me at the corner. ______
6. Wash the dishes, please. ______
7. I love this song! ______
8. Carla won a new bicycle! ______
9. Please walk faster. ______
10. I don't like spiders! ______
11. Come with me to the gift shop. ______
12. We want more! ______

Name ______________________________

LESSON

3 Commands and Exclamations

Part 1

Choose the word that best completes each sentence. Write the word on the line.

Example: ___Listen___ to the coach.
(listen, Listen)

1. ______________ the ball to the goal.
(kick, Kick)

2. ______________ after the ball.
(run, Run)

3. ______________ blocked the kick!
(she, She)

4. ______________ want our team to win!
(we, We)

Part 2

Write a period or an exclamation point to complete each sentence.

Example: Sara is a great player!______

1. Pass the ball to me ______

2. She scored ______

3. Kick the ball to Rachel ______

4. I love soccer ______

Name ___________________________

LESSON

4 The Subject of a Sentence

Underline the subject of each sentence.

Example: The sun is shining.

1. The children are on the beach.
2. I like the beach.
3. The water is warm.
4. Boys and girls play in the sand.
5. The ocean is blue.
6. Some waves are big.
7. The weather is warm.
8. John and Miguel are playing with a ball.

Name ______________________________

LESSON

4 The Subject of a Sentence

Underline the subject of each sentence.

Example: The family goes to the mountains.

1. They are having fun.
2. Wanda is eating an apple.
3. The cabin is near a lake.
4. Mother likes to read the newspaper.
5. The girls are fishing.
6. The fish are in the water.
7. Father saw a bird.
8. Mother and Father will cook the food.

Name ______________________________

LESSON

5 The Predicate of a Sentence

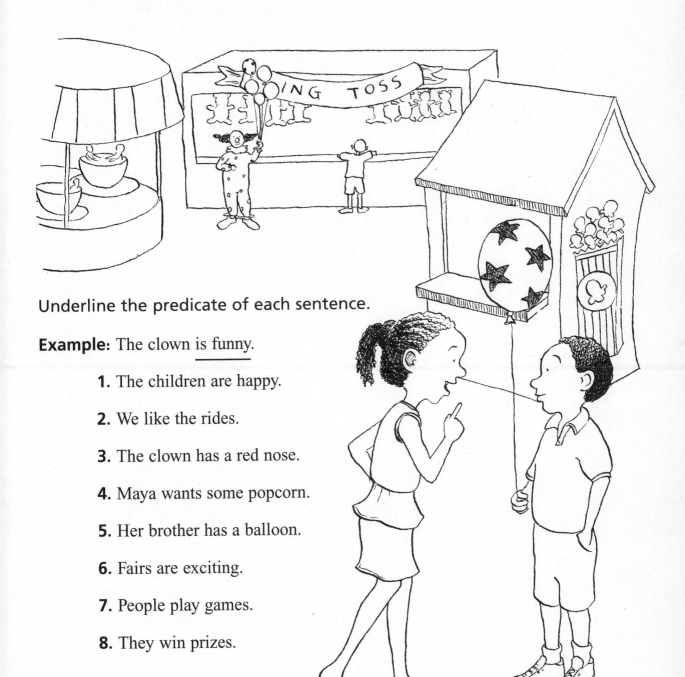

Underline the predicate of each sentence.

Example: The clown is funny.

1. The children are happy.
2. We like the rides.
3. The clown has a red nose.
4. Maya wants some popcorn.
5. Her brother has a balloon.
6. Fairs are exciting.
7. People play games.
8. They win prizes.

Name ____________________

LESSON

5 The Predicate of a Sentence

ON YOUR OWN

Cut up the subject and predicate strips below. Combine the strips to form sentences.

Example: The children | are ready.

Subjects	**Predicates**
The swimmers	jumps in the water.
A coach	teaches some children.
The pool	swims well.
They	has a diving board.
Brandon	are having fun.
Jana	follow the safety rules.

Name ______________________________

LESSON

6 Correcting Run-on Sentences

Part 1

Add the correct end mark to each sentence. Use a period, an exclamation point, or a question mark.

Example: I like to swim in the ocean .____

1. Where do you live ____

2. Please close the window ____

3. Alberto hit a huge home run ____

Part 2

Correct each run-on sentence. Write the new sentences on the lines.

Example: Erica swims fast she takes lessons.

Erica swims fast. She takes lessons.

1. Alberto likes baseball he is a good player.

____

____

2. I live in a big house the house is in the country.

____

____

3. Where is my sweater it's cold in here.

____

____

Name ________________________________

LESSON

6 Correcting Run-on Sentences

ON YOUR OWN

Correct each run-on sentence. Write the new sentences on the lines.

Example: It is a sunny day it is warm. It is a sunny day. It is warm.

1. The rose is pretty is it red?

____

____

2. He sits in the garden he reads a book.

____

____

3. Where is Mr. Murray he is in the garden.

____

____

4. What is Monica doing she is watering the flowers.

____

____

5. This flower smells nice may I have it?

____

____

Name ______________________________

Test Practice

Choose the correct end mark for each sentence. Circle the letter for that answer.

Example: Please clean your room
(**A**) . **B** ? **C** ! **D** None

1 Where are my new shoes
A ! **B** . **C** ? **D** None

2 This is a great book
F ? **G** ! **H** . **J** None

3 Please help your father wash the car
A . **B** ! **C** ? **D** None

4 Where is the cat
F ! **G** . **H** ? **J** None

5 The cat is sleeping under my bed
A ? **B** ! **C** . **D** None

6 Eduardo hit a home run
F ! **G** ? **H** . **J** None

7 His name is Kevin
A . **B** ? **C** ! **D** None

8 Do you like tacos
F ! **G** ? **H** . **J** None

9 Return these books to the library
A ! **B** . **C** ? **D** None

10 My mother works in an office
F . **G** ? **H** ! **J** None

Name ____________________

Test Practice *continued*

Read the passage and look at the numbered, underlined parts. Choose the correct way to write each underlined part. If the part is already correct, choose the last answer, "Correct as it is." Circle the letter for the answer you choose.

Spiders work hard for their food they **(Example)** spend hours spinning and mending their webs. the **(11)** threads of the web are made of silk. Where do spiders get the silk It **(12)** comes from their bodies. The threads are sticky, and insects **(13)** get stuck on them. The web vibrates as an insect tries to get free? The **(14)** spider quickly locates the prey, it **(15)** wraps the insect in silk to store for a later meal.

Example

Ⓐ food. They
B food, they
C food. they
D Correct as it is

11 A webs the
B webs but the
C webs. The
D Correct as it is

12 F silk. It
G silk? It
H silk! It
J Correct as it is

13 A sticky insects
B sticky and insects
C sticky, insects
D Correct as it is

14 F free. the
G free? and the
H free. The
J Correct as it is

15 A prey, It
B prey, and it
C prey it
D Correct as it is

Name ______________________________

LESSON

1 What Are Nouns?

Underline the noun or nouns in each sentence. Then write the nouns on the lines.

Example: The circus is fun. ____circus____

1. The elephant is big and gray. ______________

2. The clowns are funny. ______________

3. This clown has a red nose. ______________

4. Two dogs catch balls. ______________

5. The ringmaster is tall. ______________

6. One lion has a loud roar. ______________

Name ______________________

LESSON

1 What Are Nouns?

Read the sentences. Fill in the blanks with nouns from the box. Use each word once. Remember to use a capital letter if the noun is at the beginning of a sentence.

airplane	**airport**	**bags**
gate	**man**	**people**
	tickets	

Example: One ____man____ is carrying a baby.

1. This is a big ______________.

2. ______________ are going many places.

3. An ______________ takes off.

4. A man and a boy are buying ______________.

5. A worker is loading ______________ onto one airplane.

6. A woman and a girl are walking to the ______________.

Name ______________________________

LESSON

2 Common and Proper Nouns

Is each noun a common noun or a proper noun? Circle the correct answer.

Example: North America Common Noun (Proper Noun)

1. Mexico City Common Noun Proper Noun

2. country Common Noun Proper Noun

3. Pacific Ocean Common Noun Proper Noun

4. Gulf of Mexico Common Noun Proper Noun

5. map Common Noun Proper Noun

6. ocean Common Noun Proper Noun

7. Mexico Common Noun Proper Noun

8. city Common Noun Proper Noun

Name ________________________________

LESSON
2 Common and Proper Nouns

Part 1

Choose two different crayons. They should be light colors. Color the box below for common nouns with one color. Color the box for proper nouns with the other color.

Common Nouns	Proper Nouns

Part 2

Now read the sentences. Look for the nouns. Draw a box like the ones above around each noun. Then color each common noun with the color you picked for common nouns. Color each proper noun with the color you picked for proper nouns.

In the example below, color **Mars** with your proper noun color. Color **planets** with your common noun color.

Example: [Mars] is one of the [planets.]

1. The Adler Museum is in Chicago.
2. It has exhibits about space.
3. Our class went there in March.
4. Mercury is a small planet.
5. How many stars are in the sky?
6. Ricky Lee wants to be an astronaut.

Name ____________________

LESSON

3 Nouns in the Subject

Underline the subject of each sentence. Underline the noun in the subject again.

Example: The trees look small.

1. A helicopter is fast.
2. The new helicopter flies high.
3. Sara Reyes rode in the helicopter.
4. The pilot flew over her house.
5. Her house is the white one.
6. Two children are playing.
7. Their dog is running.
8. A man is pointing at the helicopter.

Name ______________________

LESSON

3 Nouns in the Subject

ON YOUR OWN

Write the noun in the subject of each sentence.

Example: The children are having fun. ___children___

1. The students ran in a race. ______________
2. Some girls can run very fast. ______________
3. Ana Waters won the first race. ______________
4. A teacher timed the race. ______________
5. A tall boy passed two girls. ______________
6. Two children cheered. ______________

Name ______________________________

LESSON

4 Singular and Plural Nouns

Listen to each word and circle the drawing that matches what you hear.

Example: 

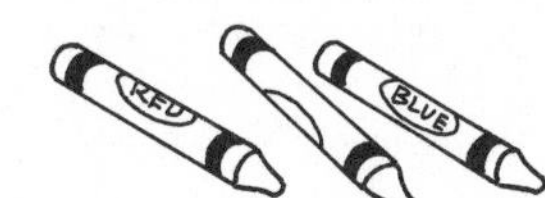

1.  

4.  

2.  

5.  

3. 

6.  

Name ______________________________

LESSON
4 Singular and Plural Nouns

Read the sentences. Underline all the singular nouns once. Underline all the plural nouns twice.

Example: The girls are wearing big clothes and shoes.

1. Two boys are wearing hats.

2. Charlie is wearing boots and a raincoat.

3. Colin is wearing a large jacket and a tie.

4. Sandra is looking at a dress.

5. Luisa is holding some flowers.

6. One girl is looking in a mirror.

Name ___________________________________

LESSON

5 Plural Nouns with *-es*

Listen to each word and circle the drawing that matches what you hear.

Example: 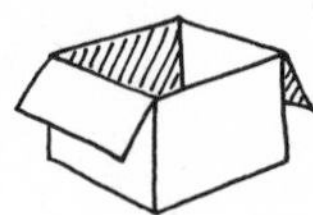 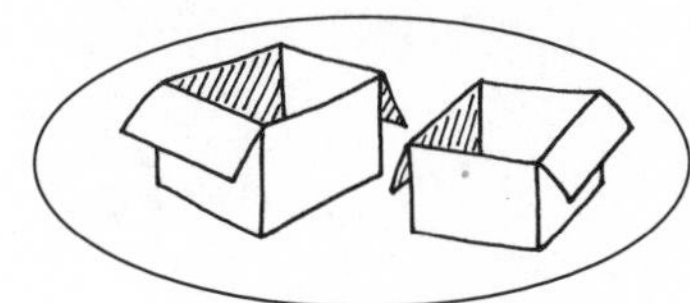

1. 

4.  

2. Kelly Stevens 1234 Oak Lane Hyde Park, NY12538 

5.  

3.  

6.  

Name ______________________________

LESSON

5 Plural Nouns with *-es*

There are eight incorrect plural nouns in this list. Cross out each incorrect noun. Then write the correct plural noun above the incorrect noun.

lunches
Example: Make two ~~lunchs~~ for Chris and Tanya.

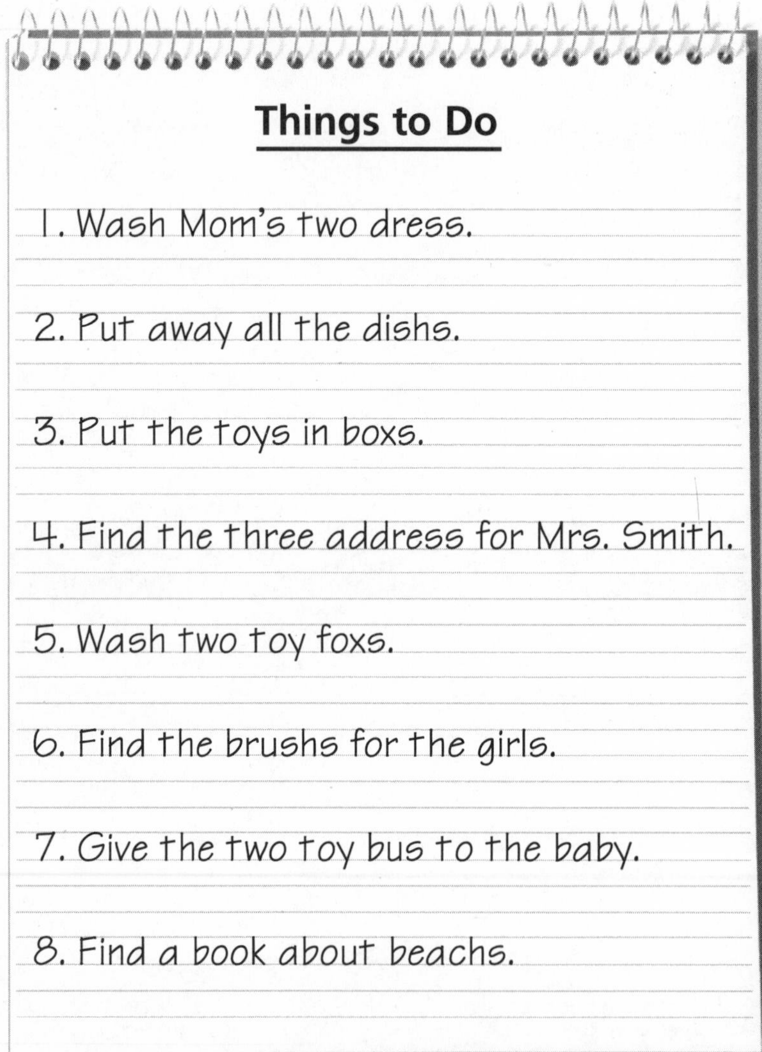

Things to Do
1. Wash Mom's two dress.
2. Put away all the dishs.
3. Put the toys in boxs.
4. Find the three address for Mrs. Smith.
5. Wash two toy foxs.
6. Find the brushs for the girls.
7. Give the two toy bus to the baby.
8. Find a book about beachs.

Name ______________________________

LESSON

6 More Plural Nouns with *-es*

Listen to each word and circle the drawing that matches what you hear.

Example:  

1.   

4.  

2.  

5.  

3.   

6.  

Name ______________________________

LESSON

6 More Plural Nouns with *-es*

What is the word for each drawing in the paragraph? Write the plural noun for each picture on the lines below the paragraph.

Example: Sometimes Joe and I sell . daisies

I live on a farm. My mom and dad raise  **(1.)**. They also grow  **(2.)**. I have three brothers. Joe is my big brother. Brian and Jeff are  **(3.)**. They can't even walk yet! I have four  **(4.)**. My brother Joe has two  **(5.)**. I am saving my  **(6.)** to buy a baby pig.

1.  ____________
4.  ____________
2.  ____________
5.  ____________
3.  ____________
6. ____________

Name ____________________

LESSON

7 Special Plural Nouns

Listen to each word and circle the drawing that matches what you hear.

Example:  

1.  

4.  

2. 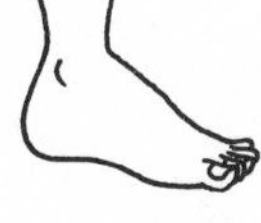 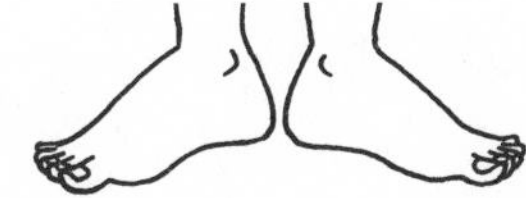

5.  

3.  

6. 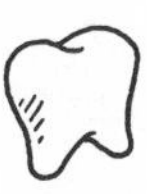 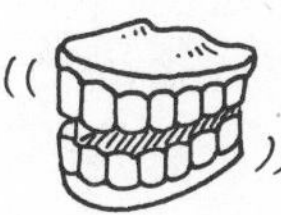

Name ____________________

LESSON

7 Special Plural Nouns

ON YOUR OWN

Write the singular and plural nouns that go with each pair of pictures.

Example:  goose  geese

1. ____________________ 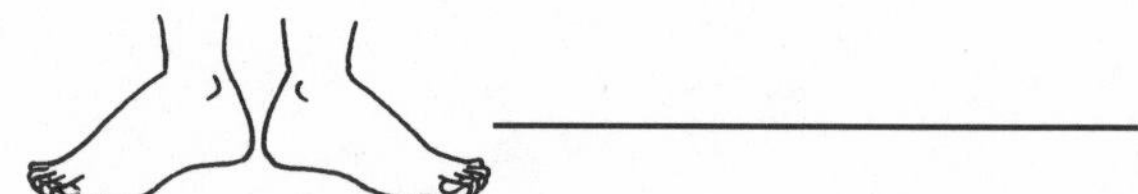 ____________________

2. ____________________  ____________________

3. ____________________  ____________________

4. ____________________ 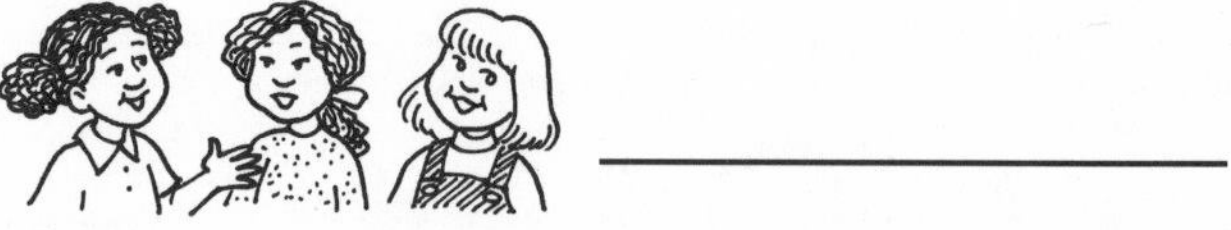 ____________________

5. ____________________ 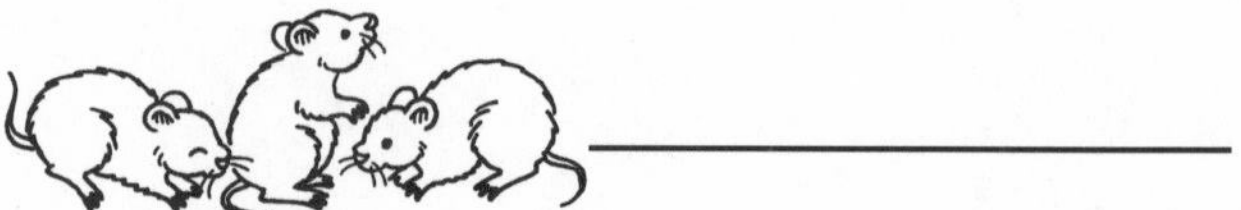 ____________________

6. ____________________ 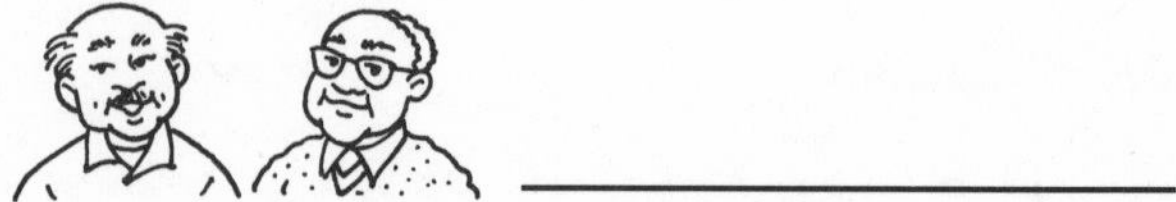 ____________________

Name ______________________________

LESSON

8 Singular Possessive Nouns

Make each underlined singular noun possessive. Then write the possessive noun on the line.

Example: the boy 's hat ____boy's____

1. the girl ____ dress ______________
2. the horse ____ tail ______________
3. the dog ____ bones ______________
4. the bunny ____ ears ______________
5. the man ____ tractor ______________
6. the woman ____ flowers ______________
7. the lion ____ mane ______________
8. the teacher ____ desk ______________

Name ____________________

LESSON

8 Singular Possessive Nouns

Complete each sentence. Fill in the blanks with the possessive of each noun in ( ).

Example: Ms. Rivera is showing a ___child's___ drawing. (child)

1. ____________ class made invitations for the open house. (Juan)

2. The ____________ cage was clean. (snake)

3. Ms. Rivera is talking to ____________ parents. (Keiko)

4. Samara is looking at her ____________ science project. (friend)

5. Sam showed the ____________ books to Mr. Fielding. (teacher)

6. ____________ favorite book is about dinosaurs. (Sam)

Name ______________________________

LESSON

9 Plural Possessive Nouns

Part 1

Circle the phrase with the possessive form that matches the drawing.

Example:  the puppy's toys  the puppies' toys

1. the boy's trucks the boys' trucks

2. the bunny's ears the bunnies' ears

Part 2

Make each underlined plural noun possessive. Then write the possessive noun on the line.

Example:  the boys ’ balloons boys’

1. the farmers _____ berries ______________

2. the babies _____ blocks ______________

3. the teachers _____ books ______________

4. my friends _____ mother ______________

Name ____________________

LESSON

9 Plural Possessive Nouns

Complete each sentence. Fill in the blanks with the possessive of each noun in ( ).

Example: Where is the <u>bunnies'</u> cage? (bunnies)

1. My twin ____________________ room is messy. (brothers)

2. The ____________________ beds are never made. (twins)

3. My brothers can't find the ____________________ food. (hamsters)

4. My ____________________ computer is in the room. (parents)

5. The boys lost my two ____________________ snake. (cousins)

6. The ________________ pictures are hanging on the wall. (boys)

Name ______________________________

Test Practice

Read each group of sentences. Choose the sentence that is written correctly. Circle the letter for that answer.

Example

A I blew up three balloon.

B He baked a chocolate cakes.

(C) Jill ate one slice of pizza.

D How many game did you play?

1 **A** Did you buy a new hat?

B All the toy are on sale.

C Grandpa likes book about gardens.

D She bought a stuffed animals.

2 **F** The sandwichs were good.

G Two foxes ran across the road.

H Is it Matt's turn to wash the dishes?

J The baby ate two bunchs of grapes.

3 **A** Josh fed bread to three gooses.

B Some puppys ran after my ball.

C I broke two tooths when I fell!

D All mice like cheese.

4 **F** The children were happy.

G They found two pennys.

H Father met two mens.

J I filled a basket with strawberry.

5 **A** Let's pick some wild blueberryes!

B Those womans gave us directions.

C Both my feets were sore.

D We have blue stains all over our dresses.

6 **F** I carried the teachers books.

G Anas' team won the spelling contest.

H I have Kayla's pencil.

J That students report was interesting.

7 **A** The twins faces are covered with ice cream.

B The babies's toys are all dirty.

C Their toy bunnyes ears are torn.

D The children's mother will not be happy!

Name ____________________

Test Practice *continued*

Read each paragraph. Choose the line that shows the mistake. Circle the letter for that answer. If there is no mistake, write the letter for the last answer.

Example

A My uncle has a farm. He
(B) grows strawberryies. He
C also has horses and ponies.
D (No mistakes)

8 A I helped my dad clean the
B garage yesterday. We found a
C lot of box full of old toys.
D (No mistakes)

9 F My sisters's friend is very
G afraid of mice. She screams
H if she sees a picture of one!
J (No mistakes)

10 A Do you know the women
B in this old picture? they are my
C mother and Aunt Jessie.
D (No mistakes)

11 F My computer has a special
G art program. It allows me to
H make beautiful picture.
J (No mistakes)

12 A My two brothers' pet
B snake is missing. I hope my
C brothers find it before I do!
D (No mistakes)

13 F Help me gather lettuce
G from the garden. It is time
H to feed my two bunnies.
J (No mistakes)

14 A It must be Tylers turn to
B clean our room. That explains
C why I cannot find him.
D (No mistakes)

15 F Bring a book with you for
G the bus trip it will take a long
H time to reach New York City.
J (No mistakes)

16 A It is hot in my town in
B July. Every day all the childs
C wait for the ice-cream truck.
D (No mistakes)

Name ______________________________

LESSON

1 What Are Verbs?

Underline the action verbs. Then write the sentences on the lines.

Example: A baby zebra ran to its mother.

A baby zebra ran to its mother.

1. Carol and I visited the zoo.

____

2. We went with our grandmother.

____

3. Carol liked the monkeys.

____

4. The monkeys played on the swings.

____

5. We watched them.

____

6. I liked the zebras.

____

Name ____________________

LESSON 1

What Are Verbs?

What are the animals doing? Match the animals with the verbs in the box that describe what they are doing. Then complete each sentence.

ate leaves	climbed
flew	ran
played	roared
swam	

Example: The bird ___flew___.

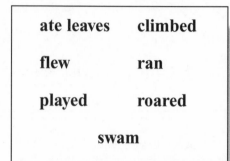

1. The lion ____________________.

4. The zebra ____________________.

2. The polar bear ____________________.

5. The tiger cubs ____________________.

3. The giraffe ____________________.

6. The monkey ____________________.

Name ______________________________

LESSON

2 Verbs in the Present

Choose the correct verb in ( ) to complete each sentence. Write the verb on the line. Is the subject singular or plural? Circle the correct answer.

Example: Marlise ___thinks___ it is too cold. (singular) plural
(think, thinks)

1. The children ______________ in the snow. singular plural
(play, plays)

2. Mark ______________ a snowman. singular plural
(build, builds)

3. Tony and Samara ______________ snowballs. singular plural
(throw, throws)

4. Cindy ______________ on the ice. singular plural
(skate, skates)

5. Brad ______________ on a snow fort. singular plural
(work, works)

6. They ______________ sleds down the hill. singular plural
(ride, rides)

Name ____________________

LESSON

2 Verbs in the Present

What are the animals doing? Match each subject with the sentence ending that best describes what is happening in the picture. Then complete each sentence.

builds a nest	**slithers through the grass**	**runs fast**
hide in their shells	**play with a ball**	**eats a banana**

Example: A horse ___runs fast___.

1. A snake ____________________.

2. The turtles ____________________.

3. A monkey ____________________.

4. The cats ____________________.

5. A bird ____________________.

Name ____________________

LESSON 3

More Verbs in the Present

Choose the correct verb in ( ) to complete each sentence. Write the verb on the line.

Example: Carlos ___tries___ his new baseball glove.
(try, tries)

1. Grandfather ______________ the children play.
(watch, watches)

2. Mother ______________ Christy.
(dry, dries)

3. The baby ______________.
(cry, cries)

4. Alec ______________ everyone with water.
(splash, splashes)

5. Grandmother ______________ Christy's hair.
(brush, brushes)

6. Father ______________ a ball to Carlos.
(toss, tosses)

Name ______________________________

LESSON

3 More Verbs in the Present

ON YOUR OWN

Write a check mark (✔) next to the correct sentences. Fix any incorrect sentences by putting a line through the incorrect verb and writing the correct present time of the verb on the line.

Examples: Patrick tries hard at school. ____✔____

The boys ~~finishes~~ their lunch. ____finish____

1. We studies hard. ______________
2. Jana finishes first. ______________
3. William watch the teacher. ______________
4. The bird fly to the nest. ______________
5. Jackie tosses his hat in the air. ______________
6. The girls dries the dishes. ______________
7. A man hurry to the bus stop. ______________
8. Serena reaches for more pizza. ______________

Name ______________________________

LESSON

4 Verbs in the Past

Complete each sentence with the correct past time of the verb in ( ).

Example: Ambrose ___picked___ a flower. (pick)

1. Joe ____________________ me last night. (call)

2. He ____________________ the homework assignment. (need)

3. Martha ____________________ a movie after dinner. (watch)

4. She really ____________________ the movie. (like)

5. Chen ____________________ soccer yesterday. (play)

6. He ____________________ the winning goal. (kick)

7. My friend and I ____________________ to our favorite song. (listen)

8. We also ____________________. (dance)

9. My mother ____________________ breakfast. (fix)

10. Then we ____________________ the dishes. (wash)

Name ______________________________

LESSON

4 Verbs in the Past

Change the underlined verbs from present time to past time. Write the new sentences on the lines.

Example: The children <u>work</u> on the birdhouse.

The children worked on the birdhouse.

1. Mark <u>nails</u> the roof.

____

2. Ann <u>paints</u> the birdhouse.

____

3. Fred <u>hammers</u> the nails.

____

4. Mr. Sanchez <u>helps</u> the children.

____

5. Wing <u>saws</u> the wood.

____

Name ______________________________

LESSON

5 More Verbs in the Past

Part 1

Write the past time for each of the verbs.

Example: hug hugged

1. stop ______________________

2. erase ______________________

3. hurry ______________________

4. smile ______________________

5. love ______________________

6. need ______________________

7. carry ______________________

8. walk ______________________

9. pop ______________________

10. hike ______________________

Part 2

Now choose two verbs in the past time and use each one in a sentence.

11. ____.

12. ____.

Name ______________________________

LESSON

5 More Verbs in the Past

ON YOUR OWN

Complete each sentence with the correct past time of the verb in ( ).

Example: Gary ____moved____ the puppet across the stage. (move)

1. Our class ____________________ a puppet show. (plan)

2. We ____________________ a stage for the puppets. (paint)

3. Everyone ____________________. (practice)

4. Evelyn ____________________ one of the puppets. (drop)

5. We ____________________ it quickly. (fix)

6. A puppet ____________________ on strings. (dance)

7. Mrs. Baldwin ____________________ our puppet show. (like)

8. We all ____________________ very hard. (try)

Name ____________________

LESSON

6 Verbs in the Future

Read each pair of sentences. Fill in the blanks with the future time of the underlined verbs.

Example: I usually drink apple juice for breakfast.

Today I will drink orange juice.

1. I usually go to bed at 8:00. Tonight I ____________________ to bed at 9:00.
2. I usually read to my brother. Today I ____________________ to my sister too.
3. My mother and father sometimes watch TV at night. Tonight they ____________________ a movie.
4. We often play soccer on Thursday. This week we ____________________ soccer on Friday.
5. I usually write letters to my cousin. Tonight I ____________________ a letter to my pen pal in India.
6. I usually eat a sandwich for lunch. Tomorrow I ____________________ pizza.
7. I clean my room every Saturday. This weekend I ____________________ my room on Sunday.
8. My brother and I often use the computer at night. Tonight my mother ____________________ the computer.

Name ______________________________

LESSON

6 Verbs in the Future

Complete each sentence with the correct future time of the verb in ( ).

Example: We ___will listen___ to the weather report. (listen)

1. It ______________________ tomorrow. (rain)
2. The temperature ______________________ 70 degrees. (be)
3. The sun ______________________ brightly in July. (shine)
4. We ______________________ to the beach. (go)
5. The wind ______________________ in the fall. (blow)
6. The air ______________________ cold. (turn)
7. It ______________________ next winter. (snow)
8. We ______________________ in the snow. (play)

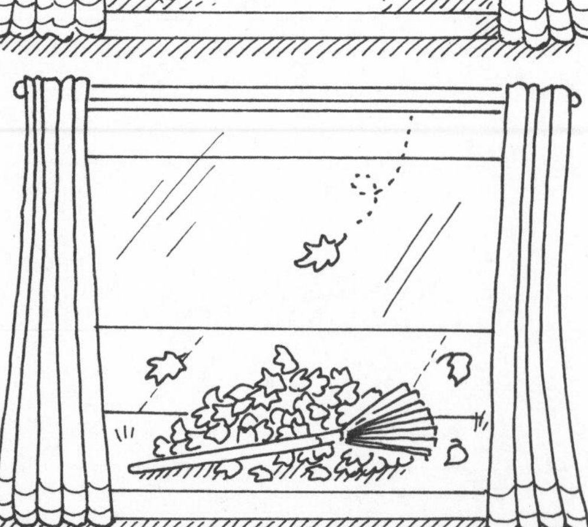

Name ______________________________

LESSON

7 The Special Verb *be*

Change each underlined verb to the past time.
Write the new sentence.

Example: Where is everybody?

Where was everybody?

1. The front door is open.

____

2. The toys are broken.

____

3. My mother and father are angry.

____

4. I am frightened.

____

5. Oh! It is just my cousins.

____

Name ______________________________

LESSON

7 The Special Verb *be* ON YOUR OWN

Read each pair of sentences. Fill in the blanks with the correct form of the verb *be*.

Example: Akemi was sick. Now she ____is____ better.

1. Bernie had a lot of hair. Today he ____________ bald.

2. Mike ____________ thin. Now he has big muscles.

3. Ann and Mary ____________ short. Now they are tall.

4. Gilda was wet. Now she ____________ dry.

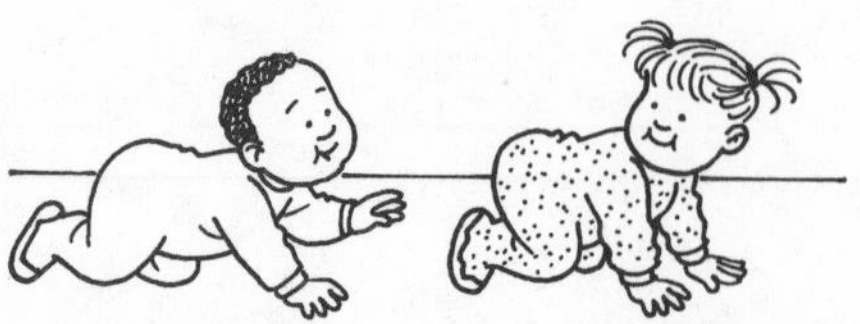

5. Andrea and Tim were crawling. Now they ____________ walking.

Name ____________________

LESSON

8 Helping Verbs

Complete the sentences correctly with *has* or *have*.

Example: The girls ___have___ raked the leaves.

1. The little boy ____________ lost his puppy.

2. Rachel ____________ spilled her milk.

3. The players ____________ won the game.

4. Cindi ____________ closed her eyes.

5. Grandmother ____________ picked some fall flowers.

6. My brothers ____________ gone to the football game.

Name ______________________________

LESSON

8 Helping Verbs

Complete the sentences correctly with *has* or *have*.

Example: Mr. Park ___has___ helped the children find books.

1. I ______________ read two books about whales.

2. John ______________ studied about dolphins.

3. The children ______________ found a lot of information.

4. Amelia ______________ learned about penguins.

5. The girls ______________ picked out a book about seals.

6. They ______________ looked at some pictures of sharks.

Name ______________________________

LESSON
9 Irregular Verbs

Circle the correct verb in ( ).

Example: I had (come came) to the stadium.

1. I have (saw seen) many races.

2. My father had (ran run) in one last year.

3. My mother and father have (went gone) to New York City many times.

4. They have (saw seen) the Statue of Liberty.

5. Sarah has (did done) her homework.

6. Now Sarah has (went gone) to dance class.

7. William and Scott have (ran run) two miles each day this week.

8. They have (come came) to visit me today.

9. My sister has (gone went) to the store.

10. She had (saw seen) a sweater she wanted to buy.

Name ______________________________

LESSON

9 Irregular Verbs ON YOUR OWN

Practice these silly rhyming chants for some irregular verbs.

1. *Go went gone* and on and on and on.
2. *Sing sang sung* and *ring rang rung*.
3. *Teach taught taught* I thought, thought, thought.
4. *Win won won* We're Number One!
5. *Do did done* Now let's have some fun.
6. *Come came come* This rhyme is easy to hum.
7. *See saw seen* Was that yellow or green?
8. *Run ran run* but not when chewing gum.
9. *Bring brought brought* and *catch caught caught.*
10. *Find found found* and around around around.

Name ____________________

LESSON

10 More Irregular Verbs

Choose the correct verb in ( ) to complete each sentence.

Examples: Grandmother ___wrote___ a letter last night.
(wrote, written)

Grandmother has ___written___ a letter every night this week.
(wrote, written)

1. The boy ____________ a sandwich for lunch yesterday.
(ate, eaten)

2. He has ____________ a sandwich every day this week.
(ate, eaten)

3. Maya ____________ a gift to Veronica.
(gave, given)

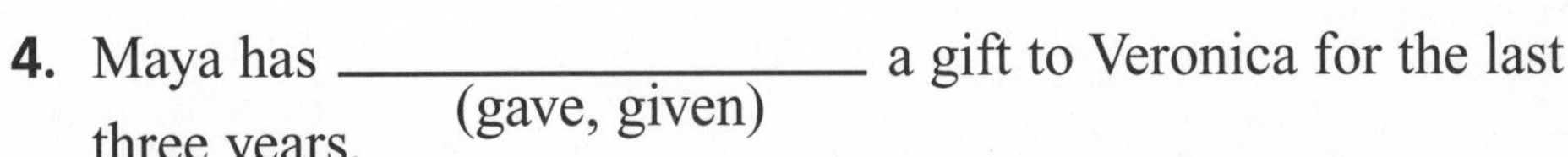

4. Maya has ____________ a gift to Veronica for the last three years.
(gave, given)

5. Mrs. Mauro ____________ vegetables in her garden this year.
(grew, grown)

6. Mrs. Mauro had ____________ vegetables last year for the first time.
(grew, grown)

Name ______________________________

LESSON

10 More Irregular Verbs

ON YOUR OWN

Practice more silly rhyming chants for irregular verbs.

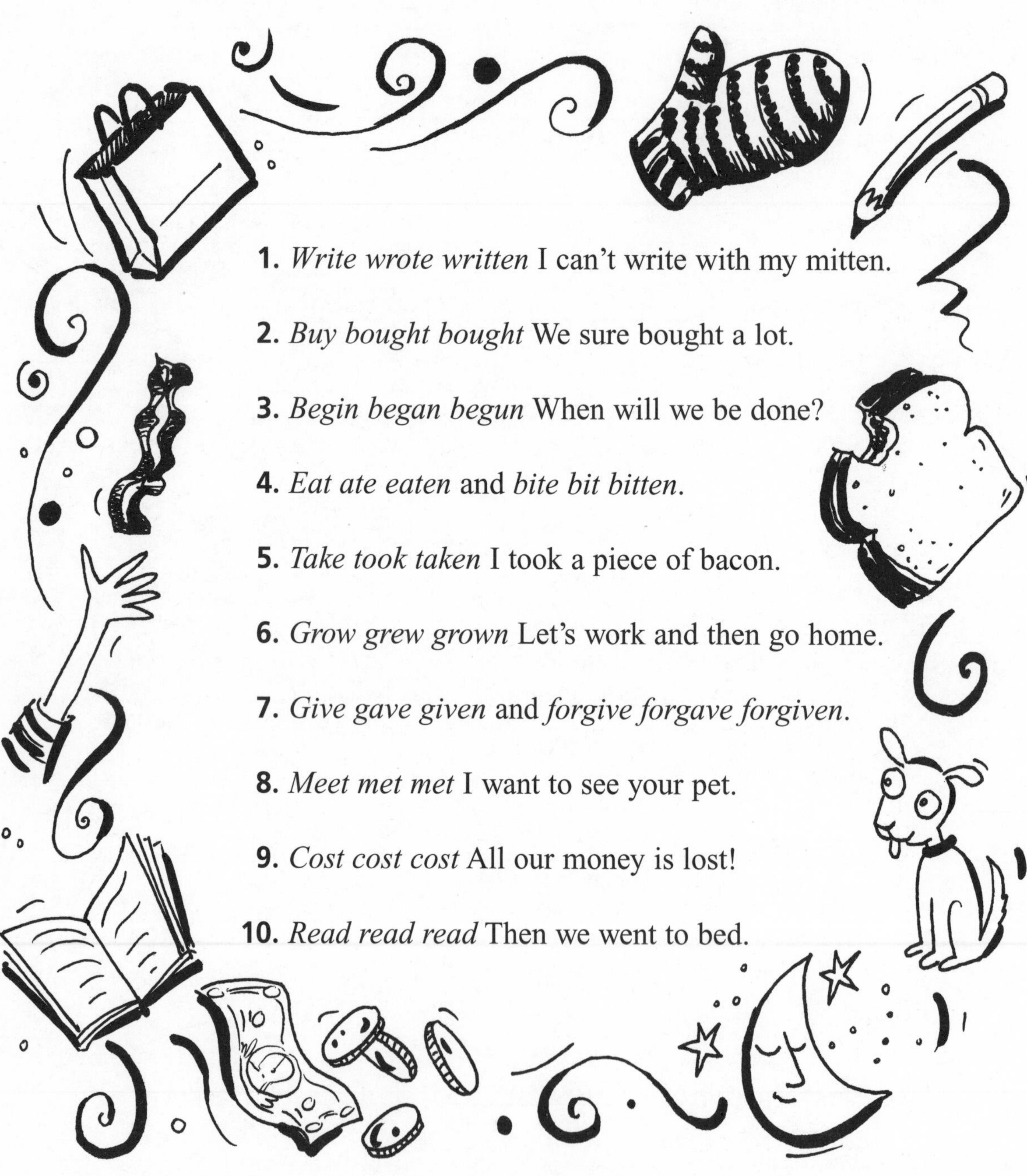

1. *Write wrote written* I can't write with my mitten.
2. *Buy bought bought* We sure bought a lot.
3. *Begin began begun* When will we be done?
4. *Eat ate eaten* and *bite bit bitten.*
5. *Take took taken* I took a piece of bacon.
6. *Grow grew grown* Let's work and then go home.
7. *Give gave given* and *forgive forgave forgiven.*
8. *Meet met met* I want to see your pet.
9. *Cost cost cost* All our money is lost!
10. *Read read read* Then we went to bed.

Name ______________________________

LESSON 11 Contractions with *not*

TRY IT OUT

Part 1

Draw a line from each contraction to its full form. The first one is done for you.

1. weren't	**a.** have not
2. shouldn't	**b.** would not
3. isn't	**c.** were not
4. haven't	**d.** cannot
5. can't	**e.** should not
6. wouldn't	**f.** is not

PRIVATE PROPERTY KEEP OUT
I GUESS WE CAN'T GO THAT WAY.

Part 2

Fill in the blank with the contraction or the full form. The first one is done for you.

7. couldn't could not

8. ____________________ has not

9. ____________________ are not

10. didn't ____________________

11. hadn't ____________________

12. ____________________ do not

13. wasn't ____________________

14. ____________________ does not

Name ______________________________

LESSON 11 Contractions with *not*

Part 1

Complete each sentence with the correct contraction for the word or words in ( ). Write the contraction on the line.

Example: We ___don't___ have school today!
(do not)

1. I ____________ had my lunch yet.
(have not)

2. Julie ____________ find her notebook.
(cannot)

3. Gan ____________ going to soccer practice today.
(is not)

4. Mr. Molloy ____________ want a computer.
(did not)

Part 2

Write a check mark (✔) next to the correct sentences. Fix any incorrect sentences by putting a line through the incorrect contraction and writing the correct contraction on the line.

Examples: The girls aren't playing baseball today. ___✔___

Trung ~~wasnt~~ in school today. ___wasn't___

1. I couldn't hear the teacher. ____________

2. She doesnt like chocolate. ____________

3. Mr. and Mrs. Nelson werent at home today. ____________

4. Mother's car would'nt start. ____________

Name ______________________________

Test Practice

Choose the best way to write the underlined part of each sentence. Circle the letter for that answer. If there is no mistake, circle the last answer.

Example: She take her little brother to school each day.

A taken

B have took

(C) takes

D (No mistakes)

1 Manuel and I plays soccer every day at recess.

A play

B playing

C has played

D (No mistakes)

2 Tomorrow my brother taking his driving test.

F took

G taken

H will take

J (No mistakes)

3 Amy wrote a funny story.

A written

B write

C have written

D (No mistakes)

4 Tina has drop her doll.

F dropped

G drops

H dropping

J (No mistakes)

5 Paul are the best player on the team.

A were

B is

C am

D (No mistakes)

6 They was in the school play.

F is

G am

H were

J (No mistakes)

Name ______________________________

Test Practice *continued*

Read the underlined sentences. Then choose the answer that best combines them into one sentence. Circle the letter for that answer.

Example

Clara watched a movie.
Sam did homework.

A Watched a movie and did homework, Clara and Sam did.

B Clara and Sam watched a movie and did homework.

C A movie and homework, Clara watched and Sam did.

(D) Clara watched a movie, and Sam did homework.

7 Kelsey plays the clarinet.
Justin plays the clarinet.

A Kelsey and Justin play the clarinet.

B Kelsey plays and Justin plays the clarinet.

C Kelsey plays the clarinet, Justin too.

D They play the clarinet, Kelsey and Justin.

8 Clara wrote a letter.
Antonio mailed it.

F The letter Clara wrote Antonio mailed.

G Clara wrote a letter, and Antonio mailed it.

H Wrote and mailed a letter Clara and Antonio.

J The letter, Clara wrote it, and Antonio mailed it.

Name ____

LESSON

1 What Are Adjectives?

These sentences have adjectives that tell *what kind*. Circle the adjective that describes each underlined noun.

Example: The firefighters lifted the (heavy) hose.

1. That is a big fire truck.
2. The fire truck is red.
3. Brave firefighters fought the fire.
4. The old building caught fire quickly.
5. A large crowd gathered.
6. A black dog ran around the truck.
7. A firefighter patted the nervous dog.
8. It wagged its short tail.
9. The firefighters took the hungry animal to the firehouse.
10. We gave a loud cheer.

Name ______________________________

LESSON

1 What Are Adjectives?

Circle the adjective that describes each underlined noun. Then draw an arrow from the adjective to the noun it describes.

Example: Roberto is using a new rake.

1. Orange leaves fell from the trees.
2. It is a beautiful day.
3. Roberto is wearing a warm sweatshirt.
4. He rakes the leaves into a large pile.
5. A striped kitten chases a butterfly.
6. The pretty butterfly flies over the kitten.
7. The kitten swats at the butterfly with its tiny paw.
8. Roberto laughs at the little hunter.

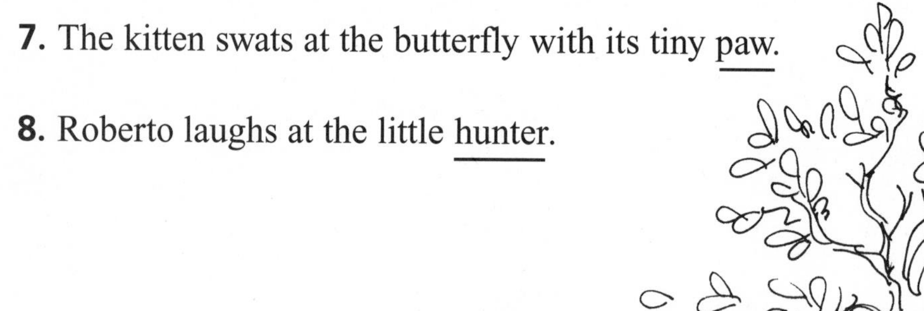

Name ___________________________________

LESSON

2 More Adjectives

These sentences contain adjectives that tell *how many*. Circle the adjective that describes each underlined noun.

Example: The trip lasted (five) <u>days</u>.

1. The three <u>friends</u> went to New York City.
2. They visited several <u>museums</u>.
3. They saw many <u>paintings</u>.
4. The friends walked seven <u>blocks</u> to a park.
5. Four <u>squirrels</u> ran around a tree.
6. They took some <u>pictures</u> of buildings.
7. One <u>building</u> was the Empire State Building.
8. The friends took two <u>trips</u> to the Statue of Liberty.
9. They shopped at a few <u>stores</u>.
10. They bought many <u>presents</u> for their families.

Name ______________________________

LESSON

2 More Adjectives

Part 1

Use the words in the box to label the animals.

bears
goats
monkeys
tigers

Part 2

Circle the adjective that describes each underlined noun. Then draw an arrow from the adjective to the noun it describes.

Example: The zoo has (many) animals.

1. The zoo has three tigers.
2. Some children watched the monkeys.
3. Four elephants are standing under a tree.
4. A boy looked at several goats.
5. A few bears are sleeping.

Name ______________________________

LESSON

3 Using *a, an,* and *the*

Choose the correct article in ( ) for each sentence. Write the article on the line.

Example: She is having ___a___ good time.
(a, an)

1. This is __________ pretty garden.
(a, an)

2. __________ red roses smell nice.
(A, The)

3. There is __________ oak tree in the garden.
(a, an)

4. __________ girl is swinging.
(A, An)

5. There is __________ old birdbath in the garden.
(a, an)

6. The girl is wearing __________ hat.
(a, an)

7. __________ hat belongs to her aunt.
(The, A)

8. It has __________ blue ribbon.
(a, an)

Name ____________________

LESSON

3 Using *a*, *an*, and *the* ON YOUR OWN

Choose the correct article in ( ) for each sentence. Write the article on the line.

Example: ___The___ girl's name is Annie.
(An, The)

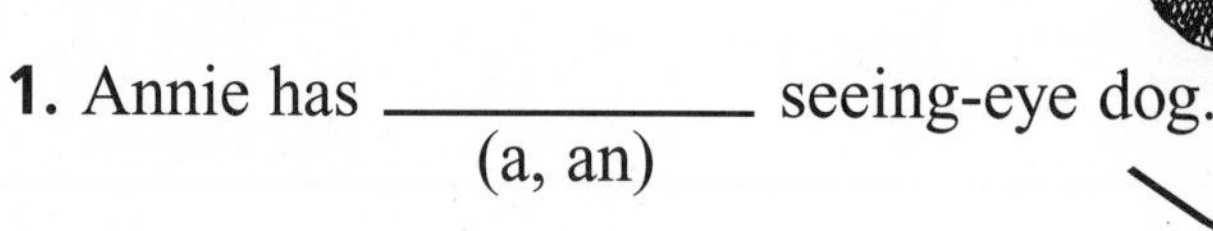

1. Annie has __________ seeing-eye dog.
(a, an)

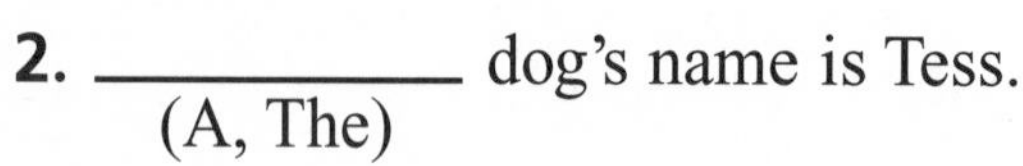

2. __________ dog's name is Tess.
(A, The)

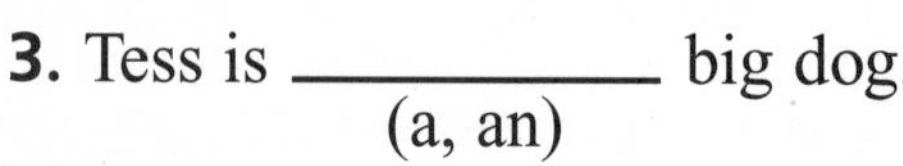

3. Tess is __________ big dog.
(a, an)

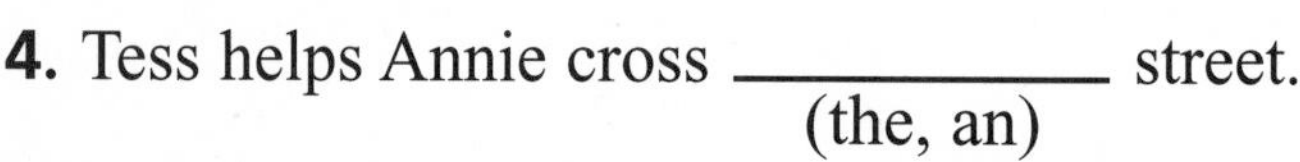

4. Tess helps Annie cross __________ street.
(the, an)

5. __________ old truck waits for Tess and Annie to pass.
(An, A)

6. Annie is taking __________ art class.
(a, an)

7. She loves __________ class.
(a, the)

8. __________ teachers are nice.
(A, The)

Name ____________________

LESSON

4 Comparing with Adjectives

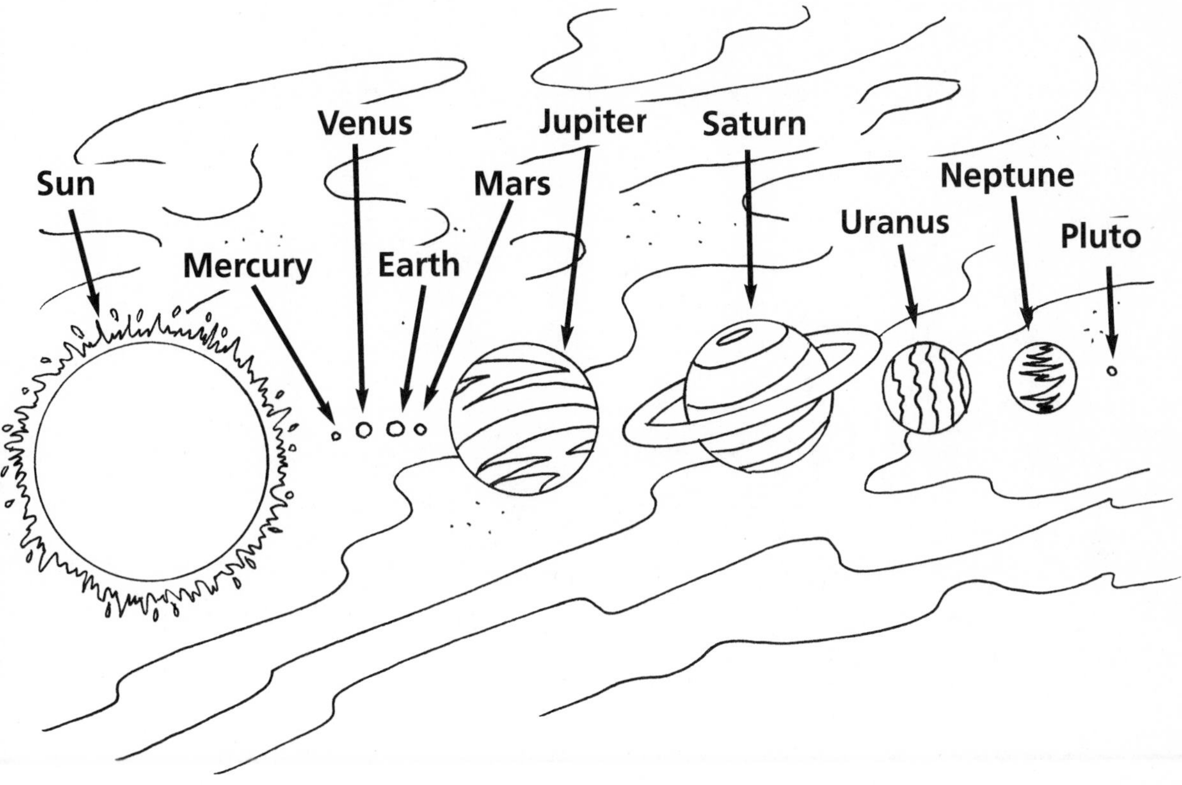

Complete each sentence with the correct form of the adjective in ( ).

Example: Earth is ___smaller___ than Saturn. (small)

1. Jupiter is ____________________ than Earth. (big)
2. Which is the ____________________ planet of all? (large)
3. Pluto is the ____________________ of all the planets. (small)
4. Is Saturn ____________________ than Uranus? (big)
5. Which planet is the ____________________ of all to the Sun? (close)
6. Mars is ____________________ to Earth than Neptune. (near)

Name ________________

LESSON

4 Comparing with Adjectives

Part 1

Write a word from the box to label each body of the solar system.

Example: Sun

Example 1 2 3 4 5 6 7 8 9

1. ________
2. ________
3. ________
4. ________
5. ________
6. ________
7. ________
8. ________
9. ________

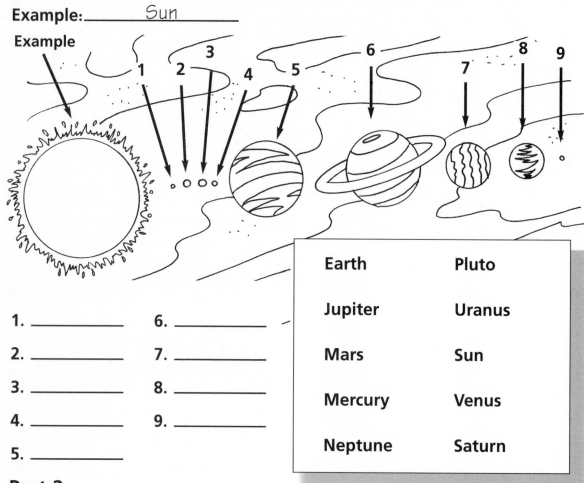

Earth	Pluto
Jupiter	Uranus
Mars	Sun
Mercury	Venus
Neptune	Saturn

Part 2

Complete each sentence with the correct form of the adjective in ( ).

Example: A year on Pluto is longer than a year on Mars. (long)

1. Venus is the ________ planet of all. (hot)
2. It is ________ to the Sun than Earth. (close)
3. Earth is ________ to the Sun than Saturn. (near)

Name ______________________________

LESSON

5 What Are Adverbs?

Part 1

Underline the adverb in each sentence. Then write the adverb on the line.

Example: The girl calmly guides her horse around the track. ____calmly____

1. The horses are walking slowly. ____________

2. The father put the saddle on easily. ____________

3. The girl is sitting safely in the saddle. ____________

4. She gently holds the reins. ____________

5. The father and daughter ride regularly. ____________

Part 2

Write a sentence with an adverb about something you do regularly.

6. ____

____.

Name ______________________________

LESSON

5 What Are Adverbs? ON YOUR OWN

These sentences contain adverbs that tell *how*. Underline the adverb in each sentence. Then write the adverb on the line.

Example: The horses ran swiftly across the meadow. swiftly

1. The horses are happily eating grass. ______________

2. The sun is shining brightly. ______________

3. The mother horse calls softly to her foal. ______________

4. The foal slowly walks to its mother. ______________

5. The wind is hardly blowing. ______________

6. The mother horse gently nuzzles her foal. ______________

7. We watch quietly from a distance. ______________

8. Nervously the mother horse sniffs the air. ______________

Name ______________________________

LESSON

6 Other Kinds of Adverbs

Underline the adverb in each sentence. Decide whether it tells *when* or *where* the action takes place. Then write *when* or *where* for each sentence.

Example: My brother and I often help Grandmother. when

1. Grandmother always loses things. ____________
2. Yesterday she lost her glasses. ____________
3. She looked around for them. ____________
4. Then she asked my brother and me for help. ____________
5. I looked here in the kitchen. ____________
6. My brother looked upstairs. ____________
7. We searched everywhere. ____________
8. Next, my father helped. ____________
9. He couldn't find the glasses anywhere. ____________
10. Tomorrow Grandmother will buy new glasses. ____________

Name ___

LESSON

6 Other Kinds of Adverbs

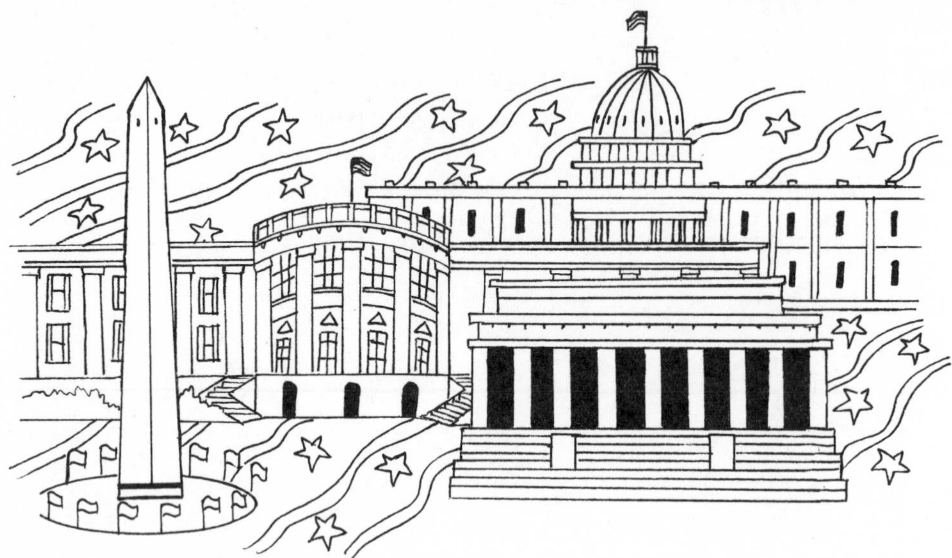

Underline the adverb in each sentence. Decide whether it tells *when* or *where* the action takes place. Then write *when* or *where* for each sentence.

Example: We started our vacation yesterday. ___when___

1. Tomorrow we will visit the Washington Monument. ___
2. The White House is located nearby. ___
3. We walked to the Lincoln Memorial today. ___
4. Later we will drive by Capitol Hill. ___
5. Then we will have dinner at a hotel. ___
6. My uncle will meet us there. ___
7. My family and I really like it here. ___
8. I want to visit Washington, D.C., again. ___

Name ______________________________

LESSON

7 Using *to, two,* and *too*

TRY IT OUT

Complete each sentence with *to, two,* or *too*.

Example: I will take you ___to___ the library.

1. Casey is __________ years old.

2. This milk is __________ old.

3. We take the bus __________ school.

4. I want to go __________.

5. Mr. Campbell has __________ cats.

6. Please give the book __________ Miguel.

7. The music is __________ loud.

8. My mother is going __________ the store.

9. I watched TV for __________ hours last night.

10. I ate __________ much ice cream!

Name ____________________

LESSON

7 Using *to, two,* and *too* ON YOUR OWN

Complete each sentence with *to, two,* or *too.*

Example: My mother takes the elevator ___to___ the fifth floor.

1. Mother walks __________ her office every day.
2. She eats lunch at __________ o'clock.
3. Mother has __________ pictures of me.
4. Sometimes she is __________ busy.
5. She has __________ many meetings.
6. I send e-mail messages __________ my mother.
7. Mother talks __________ me about her work.
8. One day, I will work in an office __________.

Test Practice

Read each group of sentences. Choose the sentence that is written correctly. Circle the letter for that answer.

Example

A My dad has an computer.

B Mia bought a expensive printer.

C Ms. Carter uses a old typewriter.

(D) That computer is an unusual color.

1 A I have a uncle named Rocky.

B He went around the world in a boat.

C Did he bring you an present?

D He gave me a old statue.

2 F Maria is tallest than Kim.

G Vonda is shorter than Maria.

H Kim runs fastest than Vonda.

J Kim is the faster runner of the three.

3 A Mark gave milk to his cats.

B My cats like milk two.

C My too cats are Pokey and Max.

D Come two my house and see them.

4 F Today is hotter than yesterday.

G January was the colder month of the year.

H April is rainiest than July.

J October is usually cold than June.

5 A Let's go too the movies.

B I could eat two bags of popcorn!

C I like popcorn to.

D I'll race you too the car!

6 F Can you come with me too my great-grandfather's house?

G He has a old flag from the 1800s.

H The flag is even oldest than he is!

J He shows it proudly on special days.

7 A Ming is petting the horse careful.

B Softest a mother cat calls to her kitten.

C The grumpy goose squawked noisily.

D Some dogs run fastest than people.

Test Practice *continued*

Read the passage all the way through once. Then look at the underlined parts. Decide if they need to be changed or if they are fine as they are. Choose the best answer from the choices given. Circle the letter of that answer.

My best friend is Nakisha Gray. She lives across the street from me. Nakisha and I have growed up together. Did you know that we have been classmates since first grade?

Example

A grew
B grow
Ⓒ grown
D (No changes)

Math and spelling are our best subjects. Soccer is our favorite sport. Nakisha is a very fast runner, but I am a better goalie than she is.

8 **A** runner. But
B runner. but
C runner but
D (No changes)

You should see how easy we pass the ball to each other. The other team really doesn't have a chance!

9 **F** easier we pass
G easily we pass
H easiest we pass
J (No changes)

Nakisha is the kinder person I know. She is very funny and always cheers me up when I am sad.

10 **A** the kindest
B the most kindest
C the more kinder
D (No changes)

Name ______________________________

LESSON

1 Correct Sentences

Part 1

Work together to label the parts of the computer. Draw an arrow from each label to the part it names.

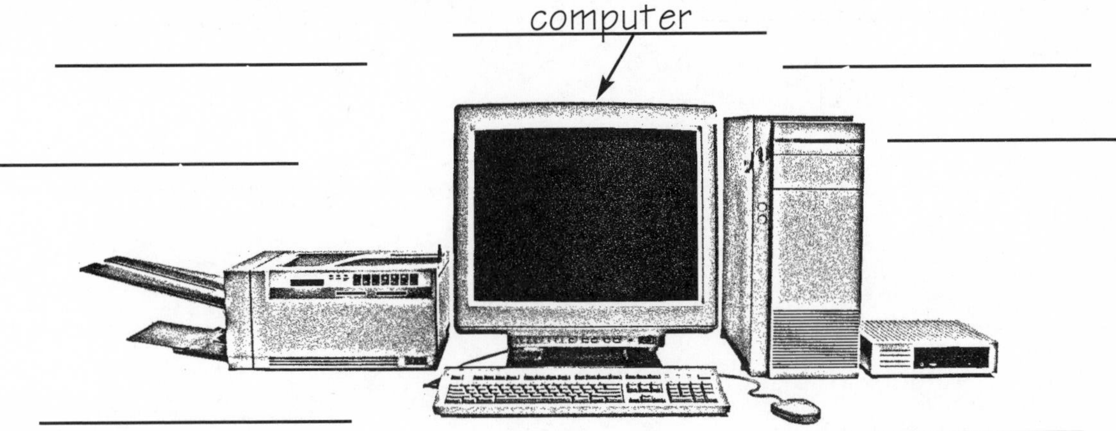

Part 2

Write each sentence correctly. Use capital letters and end marks.

Example: the games are on CD-ROMs

The games are on CD-ROMs.

1. this is my new computer

____

2. do you have a computer

____

3. move the mouse carefully

____

4. this color printer is great

____

Name ____________________

LESSON

1 Correct Sentences

Write each sentence correctly.

Example: we have three computers in our classroom

We have three computers in our classroom.

1. is your school on the Internet

____

2. we love getting e-mail

____

3. visit my school's Web site

____

4. our class wrote stories for the Web site

____

5. did you draw pictures too

____

6. the Internet has lots of information

____

7. computers make homework easy

____

8. send me another e-mail soon

____

Name ____________________

LESSON

2 Capitalizing Proper Nouns

TRY IT OUT

Which nouns should have capital letters?
Write each sentence correctly.

Example: I saw denise at the store.

I saw Denise at the store.

1. On sunday we go to the movies.

____

2. We visited uncle bill.

____

3. My birthday is in may.

____

4. My brother's name is eric w. mendez.

____

5. My aunt has a cat named fluffy.

____

6. Are we going to see grandfather today?

____

7. Elena's favorite holiday is labor day.

____

8. The best day of the week is friday.

____

Name ______________________________

LESSON

2 Capitalizing Proper Nouns

Which nouns should have capital letters? Write each sentence correctly.

Example: What holiday is may 30?

What holiday is May 30?

1. When is new year's day?

____

2. It is january 1.

____

3. Our school is closed on presidents' day.

____

4. My father marches in a parade on memorial day.

____

5. After the parade, we visit uncle ernie.

____

6. What foods do you eat on thanksgiving day?

____

Name ______________________________

LESSON

3 Capitalizing Other Nouns

Which nouns should have capital letters? Write each sentence correctly.

Example: I live on redwood road.

I live on Redwood Road.

1. John lives in new mexico.

____

2. He lives in santa fe.

____

3. John and Maria go to alameda elementary school.

____

4. They like to visit bandelier national monument.

____

5. Tai-Ming lives in california.

____

6. He can see the pacific ocean from his house.

____

7. Tai-Ming goes to school on powell street.

____

8. He likes to ride across the golden gate bridge.

____

Name ____________________

LESSON

3 Capitalizing Other Nouns

Which nouns should have capital letters? Write each sentence correctly.

Example: Have you ever seen the atlantic ocean?

Have you ever seen the Atlantic Ocean?

1. My neighbors are from mexico.

____

2. They lived in mexico city.

____

3. They live in new jersey now.

____

4. Their address is 207 long acre drive.

____

5. They want to visit canada.

____

6. Min is from vietnam.

____

7. Now she lives in colorado.

____

8. Min wants to go to yellowstone national park.

____

Name ____________________

LESSON

4 Abbreviations

Part 1

Write each name and abbreviation correctly on the line.

Example: ms Garcia Ms. Garcia

1. sept ____________

2. nov ____________

3. dr Mark Richards ____________

4. mon ____________

5. mr Alex Sanchez ____________

6. aug ____________

7. fri ____________

8. miss Tamaki Sato ____________

9. jan ____________

10. mrs Samara Johnson ____________

Part 2

Write the correct abbreviation for each day and month.

Example: Thursday Thurs.

11. February ____________

12. December ____________

13. Tuesday ____________

14. April ____________

15. Wednesday ____________

16. March ____________

17. Sunday ____________

18. October ____________

Name ______________________________

LESSON

4 Abbreviations ON YOUR OWN

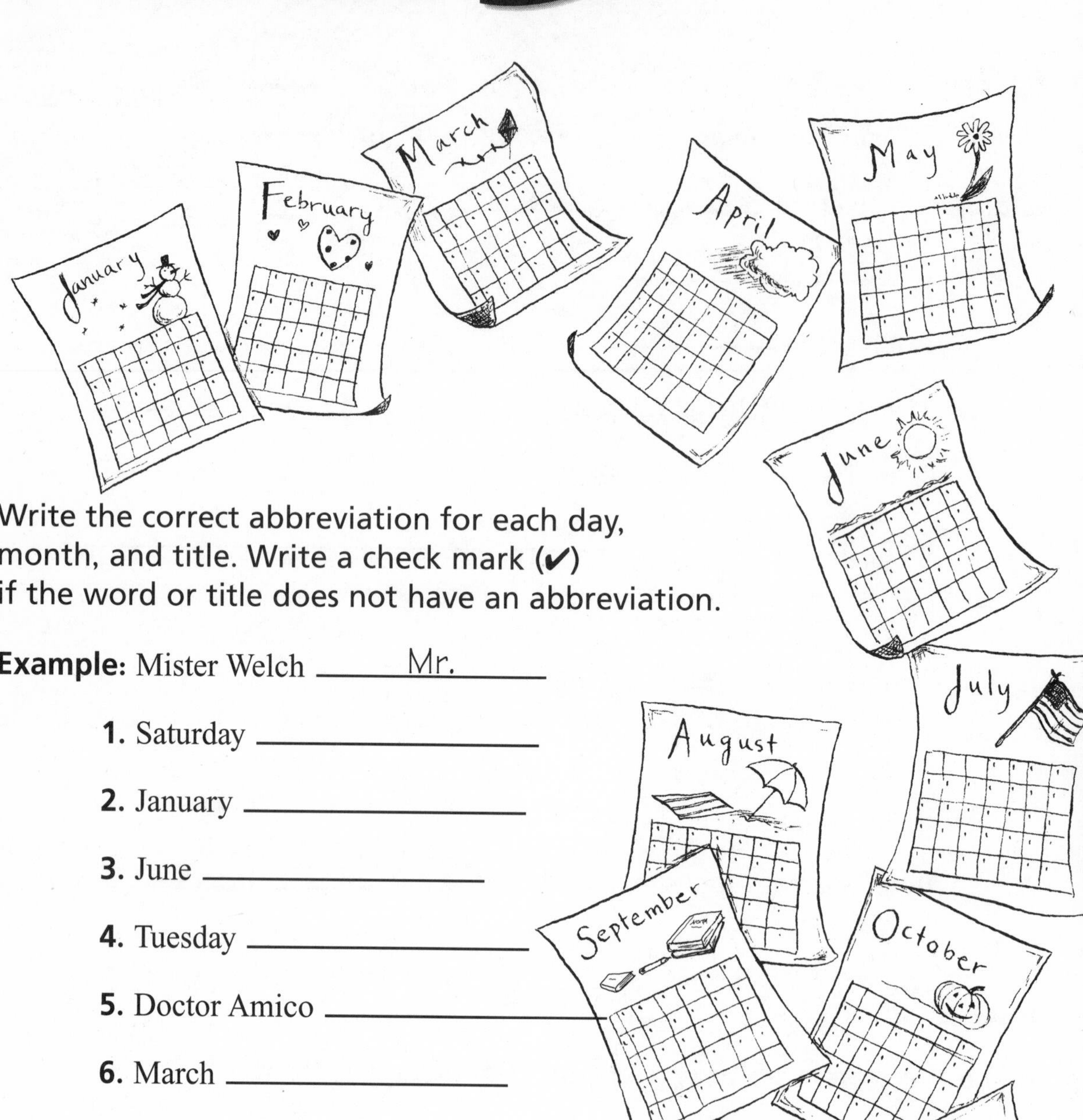

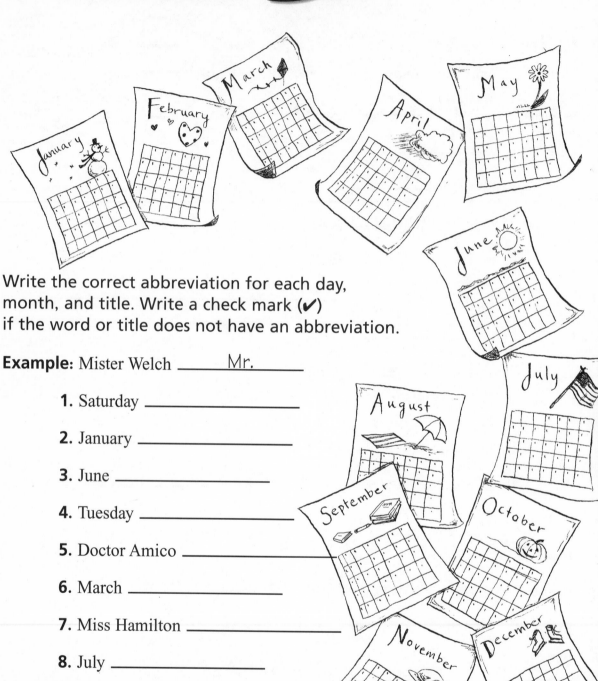

Write the correct abbreviation for each day, month, and title. Write a check mark (✔) if the word or title does not have an abbreviation.

Example: Mister Welch ___Mr.___

1. Saturday ______________
2. January ______________
3. June ______________
4. Tuesday ______________
5. Doctor Amico ______________
6. March ______________
7. Miss Hamilton ______________
8. July ______________
9. Thursday ______________
10. May ______________

Name ______________________________

LESSON

5 Book Titles

Write each book title correctly on the line. Add underlines and capital letters as needed.

Example: the wizard of oz

The Wizard of Oz

1. ramona and her mother

____

2. the waterfall

____

3. the first starry night

____

4. chicken soup with rice

____

5. the velveteen rabbit

____

6. the garden of abdul gasazi

____

Name ______________________

LESSON

5 Book Titles

ON YOUR OWN

Write each book title correctly.

Example: yunmi and Halmoni's Trip

Yunmi and Halmoni's Trip

1. Harry Potter and the sorcerer's stone

____

2. Poppa's New pants

____

3. Rabbit races with turtle

____

4. Harold and the Purple Crayon

____

5. When Jo Louis won the Title

____

6. Mufaro's beautiful daughters

____

Name ______________________________

LESSON

6 Introductory Words

Read the sentences. Write *correct* if the sentence is correct. Write each incorrect sentence correctly. Add commas where they are needed.

Example: First the dog ran under the ladder.

First, the dog ran under the ladder.

1. Then the ladder tipped over.

____

2. Next the paint can fell on the floor.

____

3. Finally, the dog walked through the spilled paint.

____

4. No the boy did not finish painting the door.

____

5. Yes the boy and the dog need baths!

____

Name ______________________________

LESSON

6 Introductory Words

Part 1

Read these instructions about preparing cereal. Are the steps in the right order? Write a number from 2 to 6 on the lines below to show the correct order. The first step has been numbered for you.

_____ Second, you pour the cereal into a bowl.

_____ Next, you pour the milk over the cereal.

__1__ First, you open the box of cereal.

_____ Finally, you eat the cereal.

_____ Third, you open a carton of milk.

_____ Then you pick up a spoon.

Part 2

Now write the sentences in the correct order. The first one is done for you.

First, you open the box of cereal.

____

____

____

____

____

Name ________________________________

LESSON

7 Commas in a Series

Write each sentence correctly. Add commas where they are needed.

Example: There are banners balloons and presents.
There are banners, balloons, and presents.

1. Nicole Katie and Luis went to a party.

____

2. The children had cake milk and sandwiches.

____

3. They played danced and sang.

____

4. Sara got toys clothes and books.

____

5. Katie Luis and Sara are wearing party hats.

____

Name ______________________________

LESSON

7 Commas in a Series

Write each sentence correctly. Add commas where they are needed.

Example: The relatives came in cars vans and buses.

The relatives came in cars, vans, and buses.

1. We ate corn chicken and watermelon.

____

2. Aunt Mary Uncle Bill and Grandmother talked.

____

3. Joel brought balls bats and gloves.

____

4. Joel Missy and Ken played ball.

____

5. My family has a picnic every June July and August.

____

Name ______________________________

LESSON

8 Quotation Marks

Write each sentence correctly. Add quotation marks where they are needed.

Example: Wing said, I like to play baseball.

Wing said, "I like to play baseball."

1. Juan said, Good morning!

____

2. When will we eat lunch? asked Fran.

____

3. Tomo said, I'm wearing my new sneakers.

____

4. Carl said, Your book report is great!

____

5. Lisa asked, Can you go to the library with me?

____

6. I have ballet class today, Erica answered.

____

7. Marta said, I will go with you.

____

8. Mr. Potts said, Please get out your homework.

____

Name ______________________________

LESSON

8 Quotation Marks

Write each sentence correctly. Add quotation marks where they are needed.

Example: Paul said, I can chop down two trees at once.

Paul said, "I can chop down two trees at once."

1. Paul asked, Are you hungry?

____

2. Babe answered, I'm always hungry.

____

3. What do you want to eat? asked Paul.

____

4. Babe replied, I want one hundred ears of corn!

____

5. Paul said, That is a lot of corn.

____

Name ________________________________

LESSON

9 More About Quotation Marks

TRY IT OUT

Write each sentence correctly. Add a comma, a capital letter, an end mark, and quotation marks to each sentence.

Example: Ping asked do you like to fly kites

Ping asked, "Do you like to fly kites?"

1. Jason said here is my new kite

____

2. Ping asked is it windy enough

____

3. Cody said let's go to the park

____

4. Ping asked do you have enough string

____

5. Jason said let's run fast

____

6. Cody shouted be careful of the trees

____

Name ______________________________

LESSON

9 More About Quotation Marks

ON YOUR OWN

Write each sentence correctly. Add a comma, a capital letter, an end mark, or quotation marks to each sentence.

Example: Cam said I ruined my cup

Cam said, "I ruined my cup!"

1. Mr. Gomez said, we can fix it.

____

2. Tiana said "I want to make a bowl"

____

3. Kirk asked can I paint my dish?

____

4. Cam asked, "May I have some more clay

____

5. Kirk exclaimed this is fun

____

Test Practice

Choose the best way to write the underlined part of each sentence. Circle the letter for that answer. If there is no mistake, circle the letter for the last answer.

Example: The class picnic is on apr 27.

Ⓐ Apr. 27
B apr. 27
C Apr 27
D (No mistakes)

1 Where is south county school.

A South County School.
B south county school?
C South County School?
D (No mistakes)

2 I saw dr Kelly today.

F dr. Kelly
G Dr. Kelly
H Dr Kelly
J (No mistakes)

3 I really enjoyed the book danger on midnight river.

A Danger on midnight river
B Danger On Midnight River
C Danger on Midnight River
D (No mistakes)

4 We need butter, milk, and eggs.

F butter milk and eggs
G butter, milk and, eggs
H butter milk, and eggs
J (No mistakes)

5 Chan's birthday is sep 28, 1993.

A sep. 28
B Sept. 28
C Sep. 28
D (No mistakes)

6 No I don't have a pen.

F No, I don't
G No. I don't
H No I, don't
J (No mistakes)

7 Mom said take off your shoes.

A said "take off your shoes."
B said, "Take off your shoes".
C said, "Take off your shoes."
D (No mistakes)

Name ______________________________

Test Practice *continued*

Read the passage and look at the numbered, underlined parts. Choose the correct way to write each underlined part. If the part is already correct, choose the last answer, "Correct as it is." Circle the letter for the answer you choose.

In april my family (Example) went to mustang island state park (8) in Texas. A mustang is a wild horse. People brought horses to the island in the 1800s, Did (9) I enjoy the park? Yes, I had a great time. (10) We went swimming hiking and fishing (11) along the beach. The island also has small animals and sand dunes to explore.

"When can we visit again (12) I asked my parents.

Example

A In april my Family

(B) In April my family

C In April my Family

D Correct as it is

8 A Mustang Island State Park

B Mustang Island state park

C Mustang island state park

D Correct as it is

9 F in the 1800s. Did

G in the 1800s? Did

H in the 1800s, did

J Correct as it is

10 A Yes I had a great time.

B Yes, I, had a great time.

C Yes I had, a great time.

D Correct as it is

11 F swimming, hiking, fishing

G swimming, hiking, and fishing

H swimming, hiking and fishing

J Correct as it is

12 A "When can we visit again?

B "When can we visit again,"

C "When can we visit again?"

D Correct as it is

Name ______________________________

LESSON 1

Subject Pronouns

Underline the subject pronouns. Then write each sentence on the line.

Example: She is wearing a raincoat.

She is wearing a raincoat.

1. I like the way the sky looks.

____

2. Do you like the rain?

____

3. They are walking in the rain.

____

4. Did she have a polka dot umbrella?

____

5. He jumped in a puddle.

____

Name ______________________________

LESSON 1

Subject Pronouns

Replace the underlined word or words in each sentence with a pronoun. Then write the new sentence on the line. Remember to use a capital letter if the pronoun is at the beginning of the sentence.

Example: Father and I will stay home this time. ___We___

We will stay home this time.

1. James and Paul went camping. ______________________

____

2. The tent is big. ______________________

____

3. Are the trees very old? ______________________

____

4. James loves to go fishing. ______________________

____

5. Did my mother bake cookies for the boys? ______________________

____

Name ______________________________

LESSON

2 Pronouns and Verbs

Choose the correct verb form in ( ) to complete each sentence. Write the verb on the line.

Example: We ___help___ Mom make breakfast.
(help, helps)

1. I ______________ eggs for breakfast!
(love, loves)

2. He ______________ the eggs.
(crack, cracks)

3. They ______________ onto the table.
(drips, drip)

4. She ______________ the omelets.
(cook, cooks)

5. We ______________ breakfast quickly.
(eats, eat)

6. Now, you ______________ the counter!
(clean, cleans)

Name ______________________________

LESSON

2 Pronouns and Verbs

ON YOUR OWN

Choose the correct verb form in ( ) to complete each sentence. Write the verb on the line.

Example: They ___blow up___ the balloons.
(blow up, blows up)

1. She ____________________ two balloons.
(holds, hold)

2. You ____________________ a balloon.
(pops, pop)

3. He ____________________ one balloon.
(lose, loses)

4. It ____________________ in the air.
(float, floats)

5. They ____________________ playing with balloons.
(enjoy, enjoys)

6. We ____________________ balloons too!
(likes, like)

Name ____________________

LESSON
3 Object Pronouns

Underline the object pronoun in each sentence.

Example: The director is pointing at you.

1. Mrs. Shepard told us to come early.
2. We were on the stage with her.
3. Mrs. Shepard gave a part to him.
4. She helped them practice.
5. The play was a success for her.
6. Everyone loved it!
7. Did you see me on stage?
8. Yes, I saw you.

Name ______________________________

LESSON
3 Object Pronouns
ON YOUR OWN

Part 1

Replace the underlined word or words in each sentence with a pronoun. Then write the pronoun on the line.

Example: I went to the football game with Dad and Robert. them

1. Dad told Robert and me to bring hats and mittens. __________

2. I gave my warmest scarf to Robert. __________

3. Emma sat with Robert and me. __________

4. She liked the marching bands. __________

5. Kayla waved to Emma. __________

6. Did you see the game? __________

Part 2

Now complete these sentences. Use at least one object pronoun in each sentence.

7. Our teacher asked ______________________________

______________________________.

8. Mom helped ______________________________

______________________________.

Name ______________________________

LESSON

4 Using *I* and *me*

Choose the correct words in ( ) to complete each sentence. Write the words on the line.

Example: ___Kim and I___ are good friends.
(Kim and I, I and Kim)

1. ______________________ went to the store.
(Kim and I, I and Kim)

2. Mom came with ______________________.
(Kim and me, me and Kim)

3. ______________________ looked at shoes and CDs.
(Me and Kim, Kim and I)

4. ______________________ bought some CDs.
(Kim and I, Kim and me)

5. Mom bought ice cream for ______________________.
(Kim and me, me and Kim)

6. Then ______________________ had a big surprise.
(I and Kim, Kim and I)

7. Mom took ______________________ to a movie!
(Kim and I, Kim and me)

8. ______________________ thanked Mom for a great day!
(Kim and I, I and Kim)

Name ______________________________

LESSON
4 Using *I* and *me* ON YOUR OWN

Choose the correct word or words in ( ) to complete each sentence.

Example: ___My sister and I___ got up early.
(My sister and I, I and my sister)

1. ______________________ made breakfast for Grandma.
(Lindsay and I, I and Lindsay)

2. ______________________ like to make pancakes.
(I, Me)

3. Lindsay helped ______________________ with the batter.
(I, me)

4. ______________________ served Grandma breakfast in bed.
(Me and Lindsay, Lindsay and I)

5. Grandma gave ______________________ a big hug.
(me and Lindsay, Lindsay and me)

Name ______________________________

LESSON

5 Possessive Pronouns

Underline the possessive pronoun in each sentence. Then write the sentence on the line.

Example: His name is David.

His name is David.

1. What is your name?

____

2. I don't know their names.

____

3. Her bicycle is red.

____

4. Where is my bicycle?

____

5. His cat is big and gray.

____

6. Its name is Whiskers.

____

7. Did John do his math homework?

____

8. We did our homework yesterday.

____

Name ______________________________

LESSON

5 Possessive Pronouns

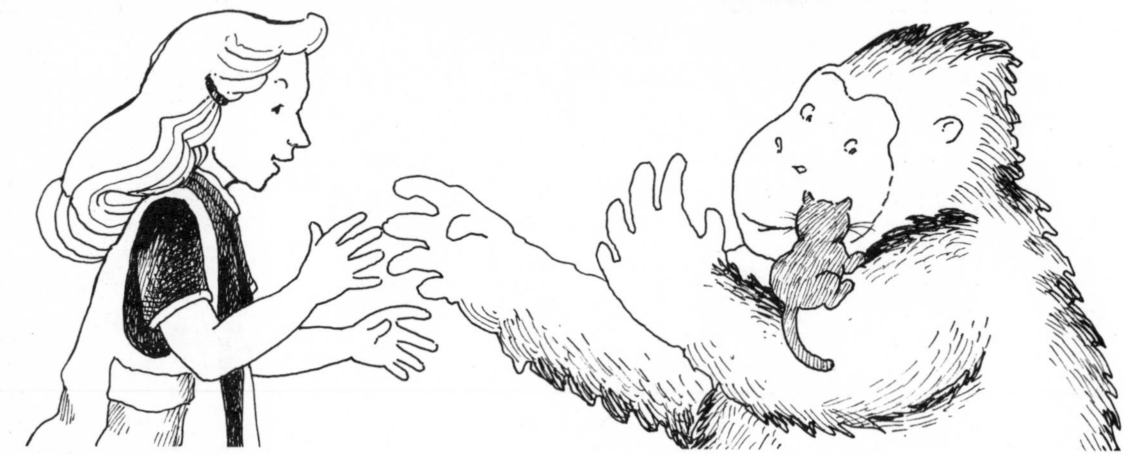

Underline the possessive pronoun in each sentence. Then write the sentence on the line.

Example: Does Koko like her kitten?

Does Koko like her kitten?

1. This is her kitten.

____

2. His name is Smoky.

____

3. Her trainer watches them.

____

4. Smoky looks like my kitten.

____

5. Michael and Koko play with their trainer.

____

6. We will tell our friends about the gorillas.

____

Name ______________________________

LESSON

6 Contractions

TRY IT OUT

We have to clean the attic
next. Come on, it'll be fun!

Write the contraction for each pair of words.

Example: I have ___I've___

1. she is ______________

2. they will ______________

3. you are ______________

4. we have ______________

5. it is ______________

6. we will ______________

7. he will ______________

8. he has ______________

9. they have ______________

10. I will ______________

11. she has ______________

12. you have ______________

13. he is ______________

14. we are ______________

15. I am ______________

16. they are ______________

17. you will ______________

18. it will ______________

19. she will ______________

20. it has ______________

Name ______________________________

LESSON
6 Contractions ON YOUR OWN

Rewrite the sentences using contractions for the underlined words.

Example: I will write a story.

I'll write a story.

1. He is a good worker.

____

2. We will help him.

____

3. She has studied English for two years.

____

4. I think they have moved.

____

5. He will be ten years old next month.

____

6. We have never been to New York City.

____

7. Do you think he is tired?

____

8. They are my favorite soccer players.

____

Name ____________________

LESSON

7 Using *there*, *their*, and *they're*

TRY IT OUT

They're over there.

Choose the correct word in ( ) to complete each sentence. Write the word on the line.

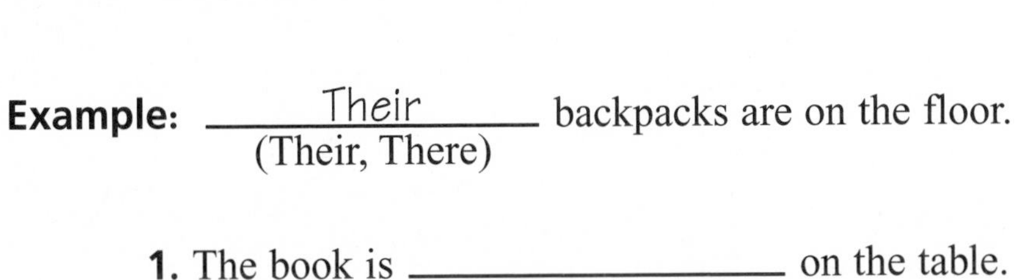

Example: ___Their___ backpacks are on the floor.
(Their, There)

1. The book is ____________ on the table.
(there, they're)

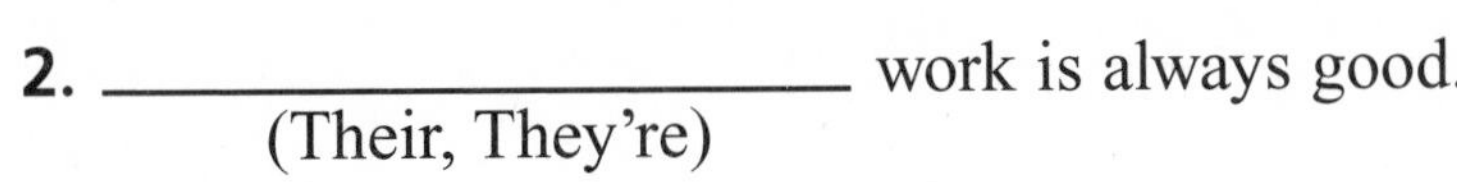

2. ____________ work is always good.
(Their, They're)

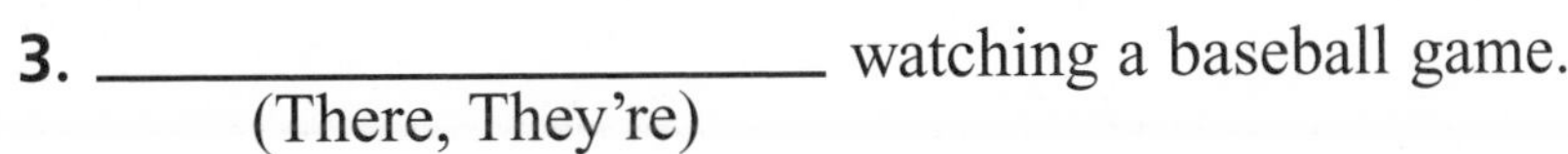

3. ____________ watching a baseball game.
(There, They're)

4. Where are ____________ bicycles?
(there, their)

5. The bicycles are over ____________ by the tree.
(there, they're)

6. ____________ doing homework in the library.
(They're, Their)

7. ____________ paintings are pretty.
(They're, Their)

8. I think that ____________ the best singers.
(they're, their)

Name ______________________________

LESSON
7 Using *there*, *their*, and *they're*

ON YOUR OWN

Complete each sentence with *there*, *their*, or *they're*. Write the correct word on the line. Use a capital letter if necessary.

Example: Their project is great!

1. Is ______________ brother here too?

2. ______________ playing baseball now.

3. Please put the food ______________.

4. I have ______________ phone number.

5. ______________ visiting some friends.

6. I went ______________ to buy some books.

7. ______________ science project won first prize.

8. Please sit over ______________.

9. Do you know where ______________ going?

10. Are ______________ cats black and white?

11. Are ______________ any more cookies?

12. ______________ going to take the bus home.

Name ____________________

Test Practice

Choose the best way to write the underlined part of each sentence. Circle the letter for that answer. If there is no mistake, circle the letter for the last answer.

Example: Keiko and me made cookies.

A Me and Keiko

(B) Keiko and I

C I and Keiko

D (No mistakes)

1 Grandma made sweaters for Pat and I.

A me and Pat

B I and Pat

C Pat and me

D (No mistakes)

2 What are they're names?

F they are

G their

H there

J (No mistakes)

3 They plays together every day.

A play

B playing

C has played

D (No mistakes)

4 What is you're favorite color?

F you

G you are

H your

J (No mistakes)

5 Pablo and I went to the movies.

A Pablo and me

B Me and Pablo

C I and Pablo

D (No mistakes)

6 I saw a movie star over their.

F they're

G there

H they

J (No mistakes)

7 Its a good day for a hike.

A It's

B Its'

C It

D (No mistakes)

Name ______________________________

Test Practice *continued*

Look at each underlined part of the paragraph. Find the correct way to write the underlined part in each numbered line. Circle the letter of that answer. If the part is already correct, circle the letter for the last answer, "Correct as it is."

(Example) Uranus Neptune and Pluto are the last planets of our solar
(8) system. There very cold because the Sun is too far away to warm them.
(9) Scientists have careful gathered data from the *Voyager II* space probe
(10) about these distant planets we now know that Uranus has fifteen
(11) moons, and Neptune has eight moons. Neptunes largest moon is
(12) Triton. Scientists believe that Triton is the coldest place in the solar
system. Pluto has only one moon. It is named Charon.

Example

(A) Uranus, Neptune, and Pluto
B Uranus Neptune, and Pluto
C Uranus, Neptune and, Pluto
D Correct as it is

8 **A** Their
B They're
C There are
D Correct as it is

9 **F** carefuller
G carefully
H carefullest
J Correct as it is

10 **A** planets, we
B planets. we
C planets. We
D Correct as it is

11 **F** Neptune's
G Neptunes'
H Neptunes's
J Correct as it is

12 **A** cold
B most coldest
C colder
D Correct as it is

Answer Key for Section 2 Activity Masters

Grammar Unit 1

Name ______________________

LESSON 1

What Is a Sentence? TRY IT OUT

Part 1

Use the words in the box to label the parts of the dog.

ear
head
leg
paw
tail

Part 2

Write *sentence* or *not* for each group of words.

Example: Buddy has big ears. ___sentence___

1. Buddy my dog. ___not___
2. Buddy jumps. ___sentence___
3. The dog big. ___not___
4. The dog is black and white. ___sentence___
5. He is playing. ___sentence___
6. He running. ___not___

Grammar Unit 1

Name ______________________

LESSON 1

What Is a Sentence? ON YOUR OWN

Complete the sentences about the beaver. Fill in the blanks with a word that tells who or what, or a word that tells what happens. There may be more than one possible answer.

Example: The beaver ___swims___ in the water.

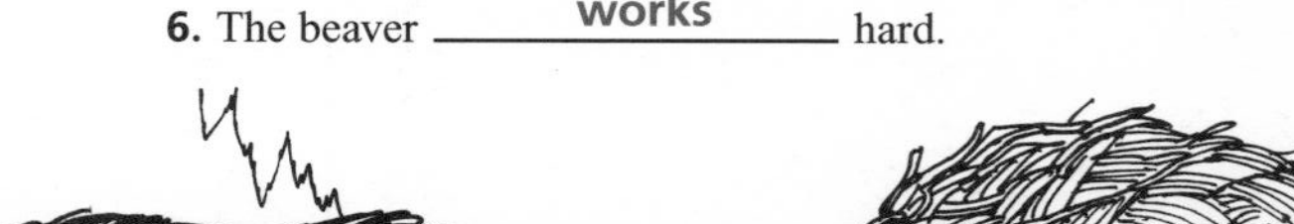

Sample Answers

1. The beaver ___has___ a flat tail.
2. The ___tail___ looks like a paddle.
3. The beaver ___has___ strong teeth.
4. The beaver's ___fur___ is soft.
5. The beaver ___builds___ its house in the water.
6. The beaver ___works___ hard.

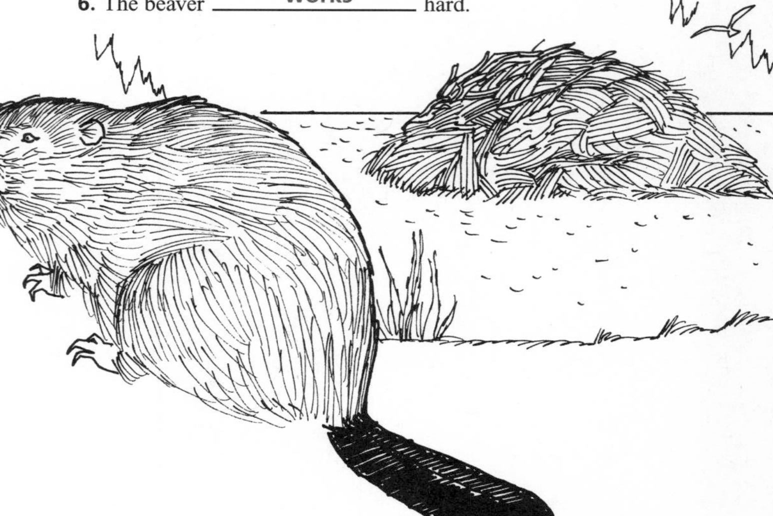

Name ____________

LESSON

2 Statements and Questions — TRY IT OUT

Is each sentence a statement or a question? Write *S* for a statement. Write *Q* for a question.

Example: This is my family. S

1. What is your name? Q
2. I'm from Guatemala. S
3. My family came to the United States last year. S
4. Do you speak Spanish? Q
5. Yes, I do. S
6. Where do you live? Q
7. I live on First Street. S
8. How old are you? Q

Name ____________

LESSON

2 Statements and Questions — ON YOUR OWN

I like to draw.

Do you have any pets?

Cut up the sentence strips below. Then put the sentence strips into two piles. Make one pile for statements and one pile for questions.

1. How old are you? Q
2. His name is James. S
3. I am in third grade. S
4. Who is your best friend? Q
5. I have two brothers. S
6. Who is your favorite teacher? Q
7. I like to play soccer. S
8. Do you like pizza? Q
9. Where are my books? Q
10. The girls are talking. S
11. Is this your bike? Q
12. My friend is in third grade too. S

Grammar Unit 1

Name ____________________

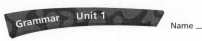

LESSON 3

Commands and Exclamations

TRY IT OUT

Is each sentence a command or an exclamation? Write *C* for a command. Write *E* for an exclamation.

Example: Pick up your clothes. C

1. Sit down, please. C
2. I dropped my ice cream! E
3. Spell his name for me. C
4. I can't find my English book! E
5. Wait for me at the corner. C
6. Wash the dishes, please. C
7. I love this song! E
8. Carla won a new bicycle! E
9. Please walk faster. C
10. I don't like spiders! E
11. Come with me to the gift shop. C
12. We want more! E

Cross at the corner.

Grammar Unit 1

Name ____________________

LESSON 3

Commands and Exclamations

ON YOUR OWN

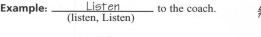

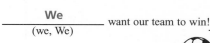

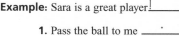

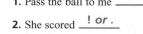

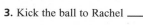

Part 1

Choose the word that best completes each sentence. Write the word on the line.

Example: Listen (listen, Listen) to the coach.

1. Kick (kick, Kick) the ball to the goal.
2. Run (run, Run) after the ball.
3. She (she, She) blocked the kick!
4. We (we, We) want our team to win!

Part 2

Write a period or an exclamation point to complete each sentence.

Example: Sara is a great player!

1. Pass the ball to me .
2. She scored ! or .
3. Kick the ball to Rachel .
4. I love soccer !

Grammar Unit 1

Name ______________________

LESSON

4 The Subject of a Sentence TRY IT OUT

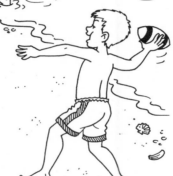

Underline the subject of each sentence.

Example: The sun is shining.

1. The children are on the beach.
2. I like the beach.
3. The water is warm.
4. Boys and girls play in the sand.
5. The ocean is blue.
6. Some waves are big.
7. The weather is warm.
8. John and Miguel are playing with a ball.

Grammar Unit 1

Name ______________________

LESSON

4 The Subject of a Sentence ON YOUR OWN

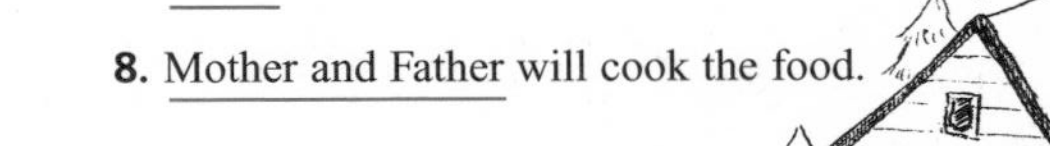

Underline the subject of each sentence.

Example: The family goes to the mountains.

1. They are having fun.
2. Wanda is eating an apple.
3. The cabin is near a lake.
4. Mother likes to read the newspaper.
5. The girls are fishing.
6. The fish are in the water.
7. Father saw a bird.
8. Mother and Father will cook the food.

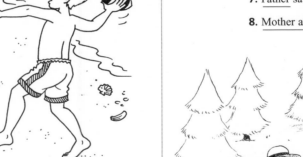

Grammar Unit 1

Name ______________________

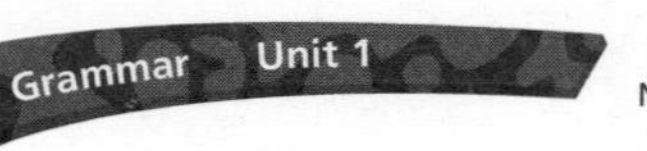

LESSON

5 The Predicate of a Sentence

TRY IT OUT

Underline the predicate of each sentence.

Example: The clown is funny.

1. The children are happy.
2. We like the rides.
3. The clown has a red nose.
4. Maya wants some popcorn.
5. Her brother has a balloon.
6. Fairs are exciting.
7. People play games.
8. They win prizes.

Grammar Unit 1

Name ______________________

LESSON

5 The Predicate of a Sentence

ON YOUR OWN

Cut up the subject and predicate strips below. Combine the strips to form sentences.

Example: The children | are ready.

Subjects	Predicates
The swimmers	jumps in the water.
A coach	teaches some children.
The pool	swims well.
They	has a diving board.
Brandon	are having fun.
Jana	follow the safety rules.

Sample Answers: The swimmers are having fun. A coach teaches some children. The pool has a diving board. They follow the safety rules. Brandon swims well. Jana jumps in the water.

Name ______

LESSON

6 Correcting Run-on Sentences

TRY IT OUT

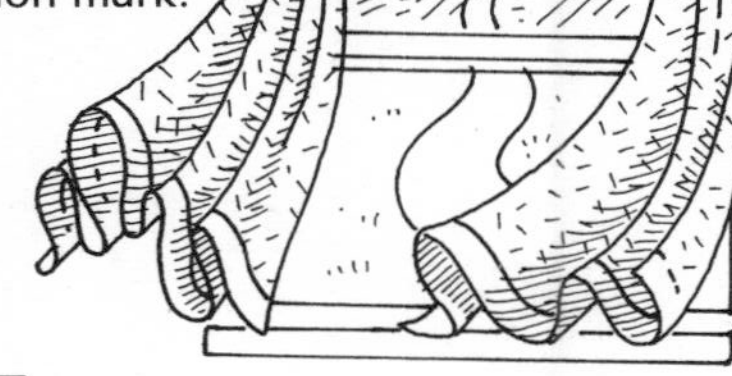

Part 1

Add the correct end mark to each sentence. Use a period, an exclamation point, or a question mark.

Example: I like to swim in the ocean __.__

1. Where do you live __?__
2. Please close the window __.__
3. Alberto hit a huge home run __!__

Part 2

Correct each run-on sentence. Write the new sentences on the lines.

Example: Erica swims fast she takes lessons.

Erica swims fast. She takes lessons.

Sample Answers

1. Alberto likes baseball he is a good player.
   Alberto likes baseball.
   He is a good player.
2. I live in a big house the house is in the country.
   I live in a big house.
   The house is in the country.
3. Where is my sweater it's cold in here.
   Where is my sweater?
   It's cold in here.

Name ______

LESSON

6 Correcting Run-on Sentences

ON YOUR OWN

Correct each run-on sentence. Write the new sentences on the lines.

Example: It is a sunny day it is warm. It is a sunny day. It is warm.

Sample Answers

1. The rose is pretty is it red?
   The rose is pretty.
   Is it red?
2. He sits in the garden he reads a book.
   He sits in the garden.
   He reads a book.
3. Where is Mr. Murray he is in the garden.
   Where is Mr. Murray?
   He is in the garden.
4. What is Monica doing she is watering the flowers.
   What is Monica doing?
   She is watering the flowers.
5. This flower smells nice may I have it?
   This flower smells nice.
   May I have it?

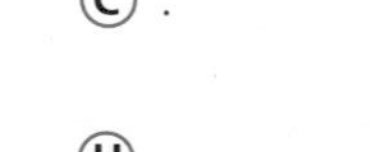

Name ______________________

Test Practice

Choose the correct end mark for each sentence. Circle the letter for that answer. **Number 6 has two possible answers.**

Example: Please clean your room
(A) . B ? C ! D None

1 Where are my new shoes
A ! B . (C) ? D None

2 This is a great book
F ? (G) ! H . J None

3 Please help your father wash the car
(A) . B ! C ? D None

4 Where is the cat
F ! G . (H) ? J None

5 The cat is sleeping under my bed
A ? B ! (C) . D None

6 Eduardo hit a home run
(F) ! G ? (H) . J None

7 His name is Kevin
(A) . B ? C ! D None

8 Do you like tacos
F ! (G) ? H . J None

9 Return these books to the library
A ! (B) . C ? D None

10 My mother works in an office
(F) . G ? H ! J None

Assessment Link Name ______________________

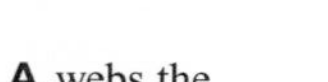

Test Practice *continued*

Read the passage and look at the numbered, underlined parts. Choose the correct way to write each underlined part. If the part is already correct, choose the last answer, "Correct as it is." Circle the letter for the answer you choose.

Spiders work hard for their <u>food they</u> (Example) spend hours spinning and mending their <u>webs. the</u> (11) threads of the web are made of silk. Where do spiders get the <u>silk It</u> (12) comes from their bodies. The threads are <u>sticky, and insects</u> (13) get stuck on them. The web vibrates as an insect tries to get <u>free? The</u> (14) spider quickly locates the <u>prey, it</u> (15) wraps the insect in silk to store for a later meal.

Example
(A) food. They
B food, they
C food. they
D Correct as it is

11 A webs the
B webs but the
(C) webs. The
D Correct as it is

12 F silk. It
(G) silk? It
H silk! It
J Correct as it is

13 A sticky insects
B sticky and insects
C sticky, insects
(D) Correct as it is

14 F free. the
G free? and the
(H) free. The
J Correct as it is

15 A prey, It
(B) prey, and it
C prey it
D Correct as it is

Name ____________________

LESSON 1 What Are Nouns? TRY IT OUT

Underline the noun or nouns in each sentence. Then write the nouns on the lines.

Example: The circus is fun. ___circus___

1. The elephant is big and gray. ___elephant___
2. The clowns are funny. ___clowns___
3. This clown has a red nose. ___clown, nose___
4. Two dogs catch balls. ___dogs, balls___
5. The ringmaster is tall. ___ringmaster___
6. One lion has a loud roar. ___lion, roar___

Name ____________________

LESSON 1 What Are Nouns? ON YOUR OWN

Read the sentences. Fill in the blanks with nouns from the box. Use each word once. Remember to use a capital letter if the noun is at the beginning of a sentence.

airplane	airport	bags
gate	man	people
	tickets	

Example: One ___man___ is carrying a baby.

1. This is a big ___airport___.
2. ___People___ are going many places.
3. An ___airplane___ takes off.
4. A man and a boy are buying ___tickets___.
5. A worker is loading ___bags___ onto one airplane.
6. A woman and a girl are walking to the ___gate___.

Grammar Unit 2

Name ______________________

LESSON 2 Common and Proper Nouns TRY IT OUT

Is each noun a common noun or a proper noun? Circle the correct answer.

Example: North America Common Noun (Proper Noun)

1. Mexico City Common Noun (Proper Noun)
2. country (Common Noun) Proper Noun
3. Pacific Ocean Common Noun (Proper Noun)
4. Gulf of Mexico Common Noun (Proper Noun)
5. map (Common Noun) Proper Noun
6. ocean (Common Noun) Proper Noun
7. Mexico Common Noun (Proper Noun)
8. city (Common Noun) Proper Noun

Grammar Unit 2

Name ______________________

LESSON 2 Common and Proper Nouns ON YOUR OWN

Part 1

Choose two different crayons. They should be light colors. Color the box below for common nouns with one color. Color the box for proper nouns with the other color.

[Common Nouns] [Proper Nouns]

Part 2

Now read the sentences. Look for the nouns. Draw a box like the ones above around each noun. Then color each common noun with the color you picked for common nouns. Color each proper noun with the color you picked for proper nouns.

In the example below, color **Mars** with your proper noun color. Color **planets** with your common noun color.

Example: [Mars] is one of the [planets].

1. The [Adler Museum] is in [Chicago].
2. It has [exhibits] about [space].
3. Our [class] went there in [March].
4. [Mercury] is a small [planet].
5. How many [stars] are in the [sky]?
6. [Ricky Lee] wants to be an [astronaut].

Proper nouns: Adler Museum, Chicago, March, Mercury, Ricky Lee
Common nouns: exhibits, space, class, planet, stars, sky, astronaut

Grammar Unit 2

Name ____________________

LESSON

3 Nouns in the Subject TRY IT OUT

Underline the subject of each sentence. Underline the noun in the subject again.

Example: The trees look small.

1. A helicopter is fast.
2. The new helicopter flies high.
3. Sara Reyes rode in the helicopter.
4. The pilot flew over her house.
5. Her house is the white one.
6. Two children are playing.
7. Their dog is running.
8. A man is pointing at the helicopter.

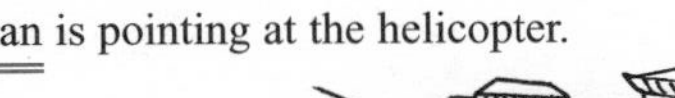

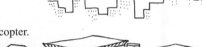

Grammar Unit 2

Name ____________________

LESSON

3 Nouns in the Subject ON YOUR OWN

Write the noun in the subject of each sentence.

Example: The children are having fun. children

1. The students ran in a race. **students**
2. Some girls can run very fast. **girls**
3. Ana Waters won the first race. **Ana Waters**
4. A teacher timed the race. **teacher**
5. A tall boy passed two girls. **boy**
6. Two children cheered. **children**

Grammar Unit 2

Name ______________________

LESSON

4 Singular and Plural Nouns TRY IT OUT

Listen to each word and circle the drawing that matches what you hear.

Example: crayon crayons

1.   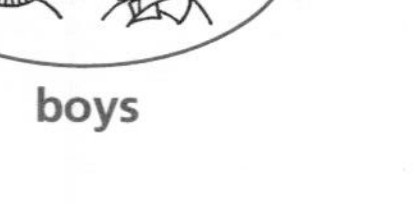
boy boys

4. flower flowers

2.    
cat cats

5. pencil pencils

3.                  

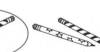

book books

6. toy toys

Grammar Unit 2

Name ______________________

LESSON

4 Singular and Plural Nouns ON YOUR OWN

Read the sentences. Underline all the singular nouns once. Underline all the plural nouns twice.

Example: The girls are wearing big clothes and shoes.

1. Two boys are wearing hats.
2. Charlie is wearing boots and a raincoat.
3. Colin is wearing a large jacket and a tie.
4. Sandra is looking at a dress.
5. Luisa is holding some flowers.
6. One girl is looking in a mirror.

Name ____________________

LESSON

5 Plural Nouns with *-es* TRY IT OUT

Listen to each word and circle the drawing that matches what you hear.

Example:

box boxes

1.

brush brushes

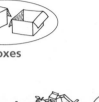

4.

lunch lunches

2.

address addresses

5. bus buses

3.

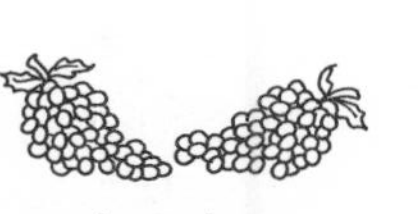

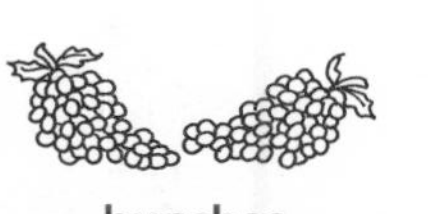

fox foxes

6. bunch bunches

Name ____________________

LESSON

5 Plural Nouns with *-es* ON YOUR OWN

There are eight incorrect plural nouns in this list. Cross out each incorrect noun. Then write the correct plural noun above the incorrect noun.

Example: Make two ~~lunchs~~ lunches for Chris and Tanya.

Things to Do

1. Wash Mom's two ~~dress~~ dresses.
2. Put away all the ~~dishs~~ dishes.
3. Put the toys in ~~boxs~~ boxes.
4. Find the three ~~address~~ addresses for Mrs. Smith.
5. Wash two toy ~~foxs~~ foxes.
6. Find the ~~brushs~~ brushes for the girls.
7. Give the two toy ~~bus~~ buses to the baby.
8. Find a book about ~~beachs~~ beaches.

Grammar Unit 2

Name ____________________

LESSON 6 More Plural Nouns with *-es* TRY IT OUT

Listen to each word and circle the drawing that matches what you hear.

Example: puppy puppies

1. baby babies

4. family families

2. bunny bunnies

5. strawberry strawberries

3. penny pennies

6. pony ponies

Grammar Unit 2

Name ____________________

LESSON 6 More Plural Nouns with *-es* ON YOUR OWN

What is the word for each drawing in the paragraph? Write the plural noun for each picture on the lines below the paragraph.

Example: Sometimes Joe and I sell [drawing]. daisies

I live on a farm. My mom and dad raise [drawing] **(1.)**. They also grow [drawing] **(2.)**. I have three brothers. Joe is my big brother. Brian and Jeff are [drawing] **(3.)**. They can't even walk yet! I have four [drawing] **(4.)**. My brother Joe has two [drawing] **(5.)**. I am saving my [drawing] **(6.)** to buy a baby pig.

1. ponies
2. strawberries
3. babies
4. bunnies
5. puppies
6. pennies

Name ______________________

LESSON

7 Special Plural Nouns TRY IT OUT

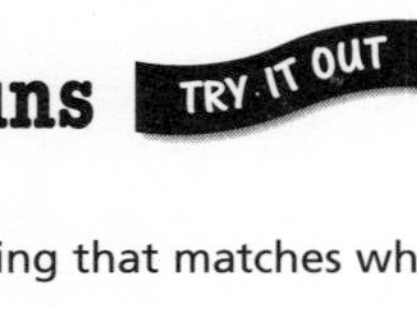

Listen to each word and circle the drawing that matches what you hear.

Example: man men

1. child children

2. foot feet

3. woman women

4. goose geese

5. mouse mice

6. tooth teeth

Name ______________________

LESSON

7 Special Plural Nouns ON YOUR OWN

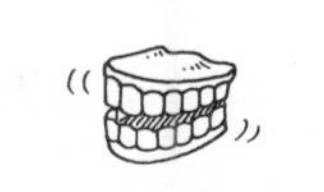
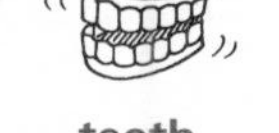

Write the singular and plural nouns that go with each pair of pictures.

Example: goose geese

1. foot feet

2. tooth teeth

3. woman women

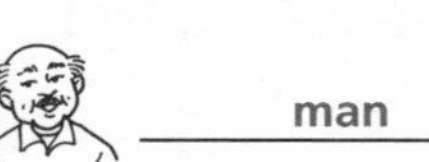

4. child children

5. mouse mice

6. man men

Grammar Unit 2 Name ______

LESSON

8 Singular Possessive Nouns TRY IT OUT

Make each underlined singular noun possessive. Then write the possessive noun on the line.

Example: the boy 's hat ______ boy's

1. the girl 's dress ______ girl's
2. the horse 's tail ______ horse's
3. the dog 's bones ______ dog's
4. the bunny 's ears ______ bunny's
5. the man 's tractor ______ man's
6. the woman 's flowers ______ woman's
7. the lion 's mane ______ lion's
8. the teacher 's desk ______ teacher's

Grammar Unit 2 Name ______

LESSON

8 Singular Possessive Nouns ON YOUR OWN

Complete each sentence. Fill in the blanks with the possessive of each noun in ( ).

Example: Ms. Rivera is showing a child's drawing. (child)

1. Juan's class made invitations for the open house. (Juan)
2. The snake's cage was clean. (snake)
3. Ms. Rivera is talking to Keiko's parents. (Keiko)
4. Samara is looking at her friend's science project. (friend)
5. Sam showed the teacher's books to Mr. Fielding. (teacher)
6. Sam's favorite book is about dinosaurs. (Sam)

Name ____________________

LESSON

9 Plural Possessive Nouns TRY IT OUT

Part 1

Circle the phrase with the possessive form that matches the drawing.

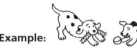

Example: 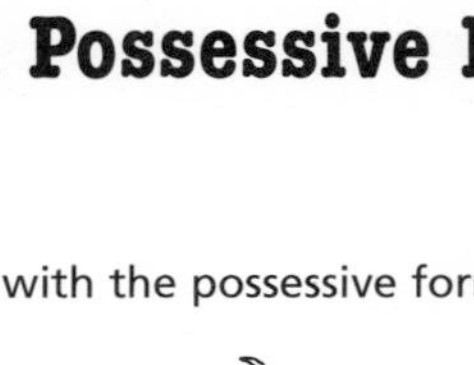 the puppy's toys 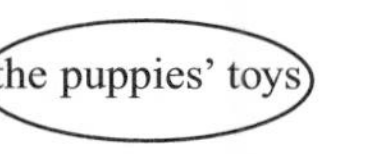 (the puppies' toys)

 **1.** the boy's trucks 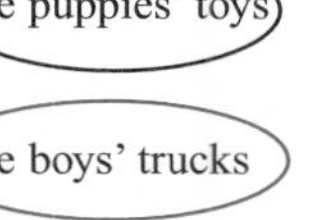 (the boys' trucks)

2. the bunny's ears (the bunnies' ears)

Part 2

Make each underlined plural noun possessive. Then write the possessive noun on the line.

Example:  the boys ’ balloons boys'

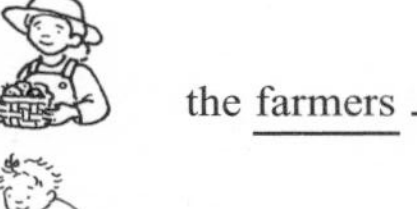

1. the farmers ’ berries **farmers'**

2. the babies ’ blocks **babies'**

3. the teachers ’ books **teachers'**

4. my friends ’ mother **friends'**

Name ____________________

LESSON

9 Plural Possessive Nouns ON YOUR OWN

Complete each sentence. Fill in the blanks with the possessive of each noun in ( ).

Example: Where is the bunnies' cage? (bunnies)

1. My twin **brothers'** room is messy. (brothers)

2. The **twins'** beds are never made. (twins)

3. My brothers can't find the **hamsters'** food. (hamsters)

4. My **parents'** computer is in the room. (parents)

5. The boys lost my two **cousins'** snake. (cousins)

6. The **boys'** pictures are hanging on the wall. (boys)

Assessment Link

Name ____________________

Test Practice

Read each group of sentences. Choose the sentence that is written correctly. Circle the letter for that answer.

Example

A I blew up three balloon.
B He baked a chocolate cakes.
(C) Jill ate one slice of pizza.
D How many game did you play?

1 (A) Did you buy a new hat?
B All the toy are on sale.
C Grandpa likes book about gardens.
D She bought a stuffed animals.

2 F The sandwichs were good.
(G) Two foxes ran across the road.
H Is it Matt's turn to wash the dishs?
J The baby ate two bunchs of grapes.

3 A Josh fed bread to three gooses.
B Some puppys ran after my ball.
C I broke two tooths when I fell!
(D) All mice like cheese.

4 (F) The children were happy.
G They found two pennys.
H Father met two mens.
J I filled a basket with strawberry.

5 A Let's pick some wild blueberryes!
B Those womans gave us directions.
C Both my feets were sore.
(D) We have blue stains all over our dresses.

6 F I carried the teachers books.
G Anas' team won the spelling contest.
(H) I have Kayla's pencil.
J That students report was interesting.

7 A The twins faces are covered with ice cream.
B The babies's toys are all dirty.
C Their toy bunnyes ears are torn.
(D) The children's mother will not be happy!

UNIT 2 Test Practice

Assessment Link

Name ____________________

Test Practice *continued*

Read each paragraph. Choose the line that shows the mistake. Circle the letter for that answer. If there is no mistake, write the letter for the last answer.

Example

A My uncle has a farm. He
(B) grows strawberryies. He
C also has horses and ponies.
D (No mistakes)

8 A I helped my dad clean the
B garage yesterday. We found a
(C) lot of box full of old toys.
D (No mistakes)

9 (F) My sisters's friend is very
G afraid of mice. She screams
H if she sees a picture of one!
J (No mistakes)

10 A Do you know the women
(B) in this old picture? they are my
C mother and Aunt Jessie.
D (No mistakes)

11 F My computer has a special
G art program. It allows me to
(H) make beautiful picture.
J (No mistakes)

12 A My two brothers' pet
B snake is missing. I hope my
C brothers find it before I do!
(D) (No mistakes)

13 F Help me gather lettuce
G from the garden. It is time
H to feed my two bunnies.
(J) (No mistakes)

14 (A) It must be Tylers turn to
B clean our room. That explains
C why I cannot find him.
D (No mistakes)

15 F Bring a book with you for
(G) the bus trip it will take a long
H time to reach New York City.
J (No mistakes)

16 A It is hot in my town in
(B) July. Every day all the childs
C wait for the ice-cream truck.
D (No mistakes)

Name ____________

LESSON 1

What Are Verbs? TRY IT OUT

Underline the action verbs. Then write the sentences on the lines.

Example: A baby zebra ran to its mother.

A baby zebra ran to its mother.

1. Carol and I visited the zoo.
   Carol and I visited the zoo.
2. We went with our grandmother.
   We went with our grandmother.
3. Carol liked the monkeys.
   Carol liked the monkeys.
4. The monkeys played on the swings.
   The monkeys played on the swings.
5. We watched them.
   We watched them.
6. I liked the zebras.
   I liked the zebras.

Name ____________

LESSON 1

What Are Verbs? ON YOUR OWN

What are the animals doing? Match the animals with the verbs in the box that describe what they are doing. Then complete each sentence.

ate leaves	climbed
flew	ran
played	roared
swam	

Example: The bird flew.

1. The lion **roared**.
2. The polar bear **swam**.
3. The giraffe **ate leaves**.

4. The zebra **ran**.
5. The tiger cubs **played**.
6. The monkey **climbed**.

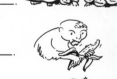

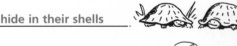

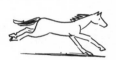

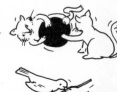

Grammar Unit 3

Name ____________

LESSON 2
Verbs in the Present — TRY IT OUT

Choose the correct verb in ( ) to complete each sentence. Write the verb on the line. Is the subject singular or plural? Circle the correct answer.

Example: Marlise thinks (think, thinks) it is too cold. (singular) plural

1. The children play (play, plays) in the snow. singular (plural)
2. Mark builds (build, builds) a snowman. (singular) plural
3. Tony and Samara throw (throw, throws) snowballs. singular (plural)
4. Cindy skates (skate, skates) on the ice. (singular) plural
5. Brad works (work, works) on a snow fort. (singular) plural
6. They ride (ride, rides) sleds down the hill. singular (plural)

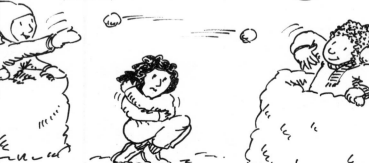

Grammar Unit 3

Name ____________

LESSON 2
Verbs in the Present — ON YOUR OWN

What are the animals doing? Match each subject with the sentence ending that best describes what is happening in the picture. Then complete each sentence.

builds a nest	slithers through the grass	runs fast
hide in their shells	play with a ball	eats a banana

Example: A horse runs fast.

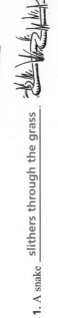

1. A snake slithers through the grass.
2. The turtles hide in their shells.
3. A monkey eats a banana.
4. The cats play with a ball.
5. A bird builds a nest.

Name ____________

LESSON

3 More Verbs in the Present TRY IT OUT

Choose the correct verb in ( ) to complete each sentence. Write the verb on the line.

Example: Carlos __tries__ (try, tries) his new baseball glove.

1. Grandfather __watches__ (watch, watches) the children play.
2. Mother __dries__ (dry, dries) Christy.
3. The baby __cries__ (cry, cries).
4. Alec __splashes__ (splash, splashes) everyone with water.
5. Grandmother __brushes__ (brush, brushes) Christy's hair.
6. Father __tosses__ (toss, tosses) a ball to Carlos.

Name ____________

LESSON

3 More Verbs in the Present ON YOUR OWN

Write a check mark (✔) next to the correct sentences. Fix any incorrect sentences by putting a line through the incorrect verb and writing the correct present time of the verb on the line.

Examples: Patrick tries hard at school. __✔__

The boys ~~finishes~~ their lunch. __finish__

1. We ~~studies~~ hard. __study__
2. Jana finishes first. __✔__
3. William ~~watch~~ the teacher. __watches__
4. The bird ~~fly~~ to the nest. __flies__
5. Jackie tosses his hat in the air. __✔__
6. The girls ~~dries~~ the dishes. __dry__
7. A man ~~hurry~~ to the bus stop. __hurries__
8. Serena reaches for more pizza. __✔__

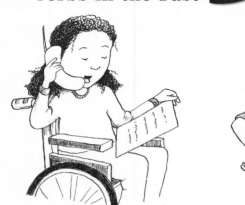

Grammar Unit 3

Name ______

LESSON 4

Verbs in the Past TRY IT OUT

Complete each sentence with the correct past time of the verb in ( ).

Example: Ambrose <u>picked</u> a flower. (pick)

1. Joe **called** me last night. (call)
2. He **needed** the homework assignment. (need)
3. Martha **watched** a movie after dinner. (watch)
4. She really **liked** the movie. (like)
5. Chen **played** soccer yesterday. (play)
6. He **kicked** the winning goal. (kick)
7. My friend and I **listened** to our favorite song. (listen)
8. We also **danced**. (dance)
9. My mother **fixed** breakfast. (fix)
10. Then we **washed** the dishes. (wash)

Grammar Unit 3

Name ______

LESSON 4

Verbs in the Past ON YOUR OWN

Change the underlined verbs from present time to past time. Write the new sentences on the lines.

Example: The children <u>work</u> on the birdhouse.

<u>The children worked on the birdhouse.</u>

1. Mark <u>nails</u> the roof.
   Mark nailed the roof.
2. Ann <u>paints</u> the birdhouse.
   Ann painted the birdhouse.
3. Fred <u>hammers</u> the nails.
   Fred hammered the nails.
4. Mr. Sanchez <u>helps</u> the children.
   Mr. Sanchez helped the children.
5. Wing <u>saws</u> the wood.
   Wing sawed the wood.

Name ______

LESSON

5 More Verbs in the Past TRY IT OUT

Part 1

Write the past time for each of the verbs.

Example: hug *hugged*

1. stop **stopped**
2. erase **erased**
3. hurry **hurried**
4. smile **smiled**
5. love **loved**
6. need **needed**
7. carry **carried**
8. walk **walked**
9. pop **popped**
10. hike **hiked**

Part 2

Now choose two verbs in the past time and use each one in a sentence.

Answers will vary.

11. ______.
12. ______.

Name ______

LESSON

5 More Verbs in the Past ON YOUR OWN

Complete each sentence with the correct past time of the verb in ( ).

Example: Gary *moved* the puppet across the stage. (move)

1. Our class **planned** a puppet show. (plan)
2. We **painted** a stage for the puppets. (paint)
3. Everyone **practiced**. (practice)
4. Evelyn **dropped** one of the puppets. (drop)
5. We **fixed** it quickly. (fix)
6. A puppet **danced** on strings. (dance)
7. Mrs. Baldwin **liked** our puppet show. (like)
8. We all **tried** very hard. (try)

Name ______

LESSON

6 Verbs in the Future TRY IT OUT

Read each pair of sentences. Fill in the blanks with the future time of the underlined verbs.

Example: I usually drink apple juice for breakfast.

Today I __will drink__ orange juice.

1. I usually go to bed at 8:00. Tonight I __will go__ to bed at 9:00.
2. I usually read to my brother. Today I __will read__ to my sister too.
3. My mother and father sometimes watch TV at night. Tonight they __will watch__ a movie.
4. We often play soccer on Thursday. This week we __will play__ soccer on Friday.
5. I usually write letters to my cousin. Tonight I __will write__ a letter to my pen pal in India.
6. I usually eat a sandwich for lunch. Tomorrow I __will eat__ pizza.
7. I clean my room every Saturday. This weekend I __will clean__ my room on Sunday.
8. My brother and I often use the computer at night. Tonight my mother __will use__ the computer.

Name ______

LESSON

6 Verbs in the Future ON YOUR OWN

Complete each sentence with the correct future time of the verb in ( ).

Example: We __will listen__ to the weather report. (listen)

1. It __will rain__ tomorrow. (rain)
2. The temperature __will be__ 70 degrees. (be)
3. The sun __will shine__ brightly in July. (shine)
4. We __will go__ to the beach. (go)
5. The wind __will blow__ in the fall. (blow)
6. The air __will turn__ cold. (turn)
7. It __will snow__ next winter. (snow)
8. We __will play__ in the snow. (play)

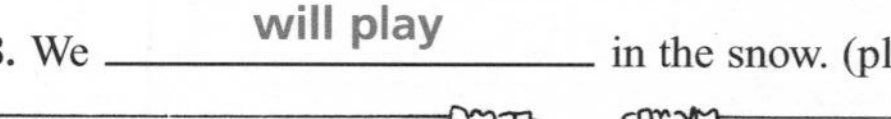

Grammar Unit 3

Name ____________

LESSON 7

The Special Verb *be* TRY IT OUT

Change each underlined verb to the past time. Write the new sentence.

Example: Where <u>is</u> everybody?

Where was everybody?

1. The front door <u>is</u> open.
   The front door was open.
2. The toys <u>are</u> broken.
   The toys were broken.
3. My mother and father <u>are</u> angry.
   My mother and father were angry.
4. I <u>am</u> frightened.
   I was frightened.
5. Oh! It <u>is</u> just my cousins.
   Oh! It was just my cousins.

Grammar Unit 3

Name ____________

LESSON 7

The Special Verb *be* ON YOUR OWN

Read each pair of sentences. Fill in the blanks with the correct form of the verb *be*.

Example: Akemi was sick. Now she ___is___ better.

1. Bernie had a lot of hair. Today he ___is___ bald.

2. Mike ___was___ thin. Now he has big muscles.

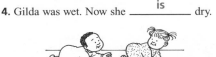

3. Ann and Mary ___were___ short. Now they are tall.

4. Gilda was wet. Now she ___is___ dry.

5. Andrea and Tim were crawling. Now they ___are___ walking.

Grammar Unit 3 Name ______

LESSON

8 Helping Verbs TRY IT OUT

Complete the sentences correctly with *has* or *have*.

Example: The girls ___have___ raked the leaves.

1. The little boy ___has___ lost his puppy.
2. Rachel ___has___ spilled her milk.
3. The players ___have___ won the game.
4. Cindi ___has___ closed her eyes.
5. Grandmother ___has___ picked some fall flowers.
6. My brothers ___have___ gone to the football game.

Grammar Unit 3 Name ______

LESSON

8 Helping Verbs ON YOUR OWN

Complete the sentences correctly with *has* or *have*.

Example: Mr. Park ___has___ helped the children find books.

1. I ___have___ read two books about whales.
2. John ___has___ studied about dolphins.
3. The children ___have___ found a lot of information.
4. Amelia ___has___ learned about penguins.
5. The girls ___have___ picked out a book about seals.
6. They ___have___ looked at some pictures of sharks.

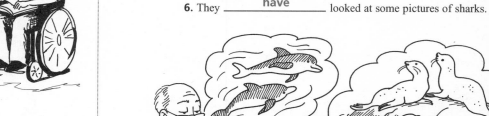

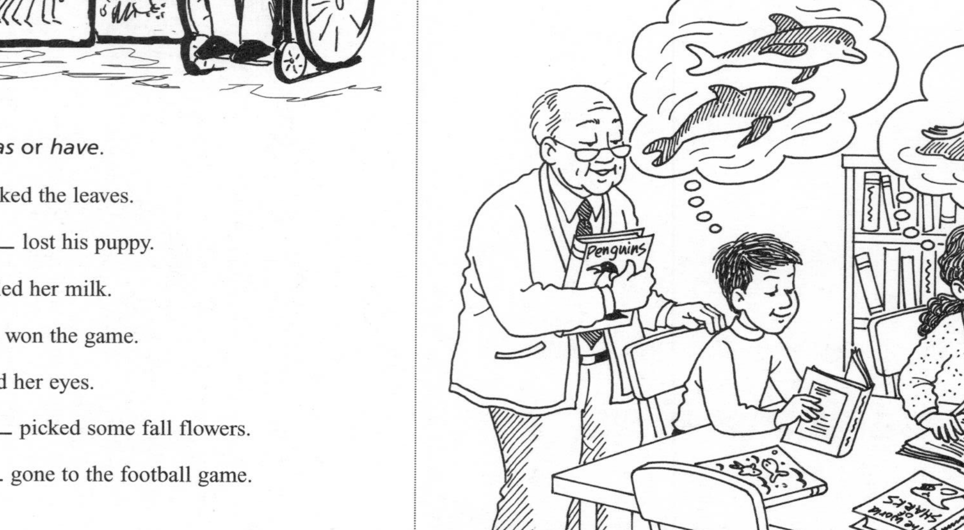

 Name ______________

LESSON

9 Irregular Verbs TRY IT OUT

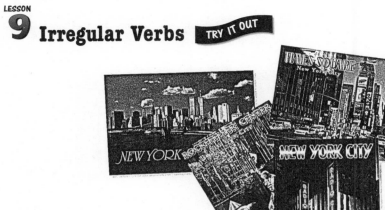

Circle the correct verb in ( ).

Example: I had (**come** came) to the stadium.

1. I have (saw **seen**) many races.
2. My father had (ran **run**) in one last year.
3. My mother and father have (went **gone**) to New York City many times.
4. They have (saw **seen**) the Statue of Liberty.
5. Sarah has (did **done**) her homework.
6. Now Sarah has (went **gone**) to dance class.
7. William and Scott have (ran **run**) two miles each day this week.
8. They have (**come** came) to visit me today.
9. My sister has (**gone** went) to the store.
10. She had (saw **seen**) a sweater she wanted to buy.

 Name ______________

LESSON

9 Irregular Verbs ON YOUR OWN

Practice these silly rhyming chants for some irregular verbs.

1. *Go went gone* and on and on and on.
2. *Sing sang sung* and *ring rang rung.*
3. *Teach taught taught* I thought, thought, thought.
4. *Win won won* We're Number One!
5. *Do did done* Now let's have some fun.
6. *Come came come* This rhyme is easy to hum.
7. *See saw seen* Was that yellow or green?
8. *Run ran run* but not when chewing gum.
9. *Bring brought brought* and *catch caught caught.*
10. *Find found found* and around around around.

Name ______________________

LESSON
10 More Irregular Verbs TRY IT OUT

Choose the correct verb in ( ) to complete each sentence.

Examples: Grandmother ___wrote___ (wrote, written) a letter last night.

Grandmother has ___written___ (wrote, written) a letter every night this week.

1. The boy ___ate___ (ate, eaten) a sandwich for lunch yesterday.
2. He has ___eaten___ (ate, eaten) a sandwich every day this week.
3. Maya ___gave___ (gave, given) a gift to Veronica.

4. Maya has ___given___ (gave, given) a gift to Veronica for the last three years.
5. Mrs. Mauro ___grew___ (grew, grown) vegetables in her garden this year.

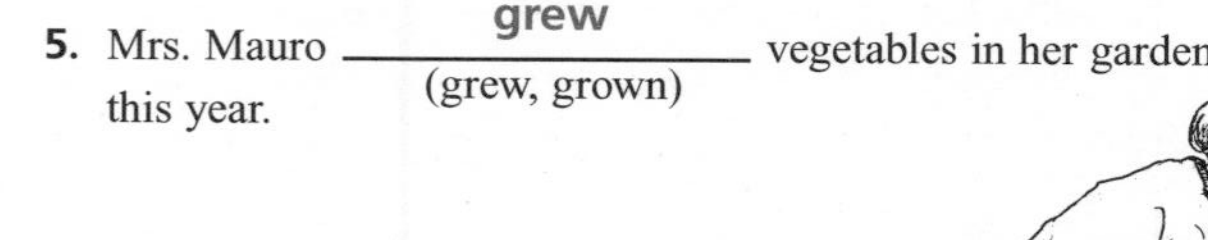

6. Mrs. Mauro had ___grown___ (grew, grown) vegetables last year for the first time.

Name ______________________

LESSON
10 More Irregular Verbs ON YOUR OWN

Practice more silly rhyming chants for irregular verbs.

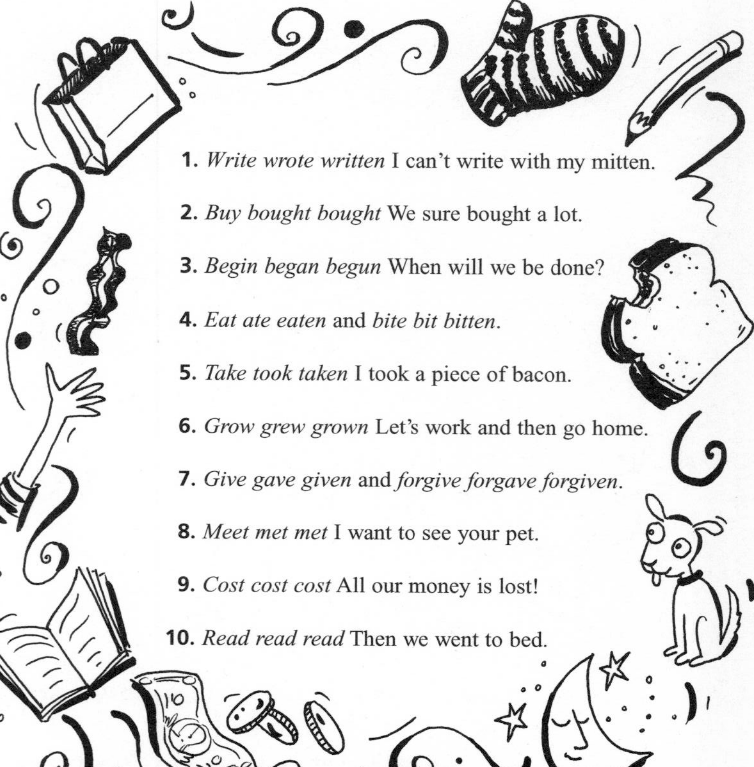

1. *Write wrote written* I can't write with my mitten.
2. *Buy bought bought* We sure bought a lot.
3. *Begin began begun* When will we be done?
4. *Eat ate eaten* and *bite bit bitten*.
5. *Take took taken* I took a piece of bacon.
6. *Grow grew grown* Let's work and then go home.
7. *Give gave given* and *forgive forgave forgiven*.
8. *Meet met met* I want to see your pet.
9. *Cost cost cost* All our money is lost!
10. *Read read read* Then we went to bed.

Name ______

LESSON 11 Contractions with *not* TRY IT OUT

Part 1

Draw a line from each contraction to its full form. The first one is done for you.

1. weren't → c. were not	a. have not
2. shouldn't → e. should not	b. would not
3. isn't → f. is not	c. were not
4. haven't → a. have not	d. cannot
5. can't → d. cannot	e. should not
6. wouldn't → b. would not	f. is not

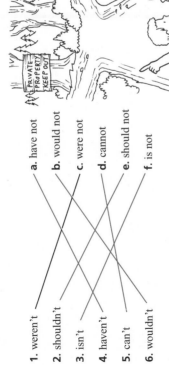

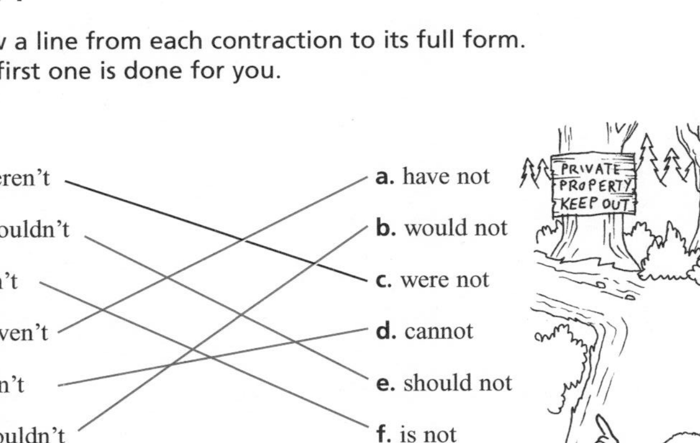
PRIVATE PROPERTY KEEP OUT
I GUESS WE CAN'T GO THAT WAY.

Part 2

Fill in the blank with the contraction or the full form. The first one is done for you.

7. couldn't __could not__
8. __hasn't__ has not
9. __aren't__ are not
10. didn't __did not__
11. hadn't __had not__
12. __don't__ do not
13. wasn't __was not__
14. __doesn't__ does not

Name ______

LESSON 11 Contractions with *not* ON YOUR OWN

Part 1

Complete each sentence with the correct contraction for the word or words in ( ). Write the contraction on the line.

Example: We __don't__ (do not) have school today!

1. I __haven't__ (have not) had my lunch yet.
2. Julie __can't__ (cannot) find her notebook.
3. Gan __isn't__ (is not) going to soccer practice today.
4. Mr. Molloy __didn't__ (did not) want a computer.

Part 2

Write a check mark (✔) next to the correct sentences. Fix any incorrect sentences by putting a line through the incorrect contraction and writing the correct contraction on the line.

Examples: The girls aren't playing baseball today. __✔__

Trung ~~wasnt~~ in school today. __wasn't__

1. I couldn't hear the teacher. __✔__
2. She ~~doesnt~~ like chocolate. __doesn't__
3. Mr. and Mrs. Nelson ~~werent~~ at home today. __weren't__
4. Mother's car ~~would'nt~~ start. __wouldn't__

Assessment Link

Name ____________________

UNIT 3 Test Practice

Test Practice

Choose the best way to write the underlined part of each sentence. Circle the letter for that answer. If there is no mistake, circle the last answer.

Example: She take her little brother to school each day.

A taken

B have took

Ⓒ takes

D (No mistakes)

1 Manuel and I plays soccer every day at recess.

Ⓐ play

B playing

C has played

D (No mistakes)

2 Tomorrow my brother taking his driving test.

F took

G taken

Ⓗ will take

J (No mistakes)

3 Amy wrote a funny story.

A written

B write

C have written

Ⓓ (No mistakes)

4 Tina has drop her doll.

Ⓕ dropped

G drops

H dropping

J (No mistakes)

5 Paul are the best player on the team.

A were

Ⓑ is

C am

D (No mistakes)

6 They was in the school play.

F is

G am

Ⓗ were

J (No mistakes)

Assessment Link

Name ____________________

Test Practice *continued*

Read the underlined sentences. Then choose the answer that best combines them into one sentence. Circle the letter for that answer.

Example

Clara watched a movie.
Sam did homework.

A Watched a movie and did homework, Clara and Sam did.

B Clara and Sam watched a movie and did homework.

C A movie and homework, Clara watched and Sam did.

Ⓓ Clara watched a movie, and Sam did homework.

7 Kelsey plays the clarinet.
Justin plays the clarinet.

Ⓐ Kelsey and Justin play the clarinet.

B Kelsey plays and Justin plays the clarinet.

C Kelsey plays the clarinet, Justin too.

D They play the clarinet, Kelsey and Justin.

8 Clara wrote a letter.
Antonio mailed it.

F The letter Clara wrote Antonio mailed.

Ⓖ Clara wrote a letter, and Antonio mailed it.

H Wrote and mailed a letter Clara and Antonio.

J The letter, Clara wrote it, and Antonio mailed it.

Name ____________________

LESSON 1 What Are Adjectives? TRY IT OUT

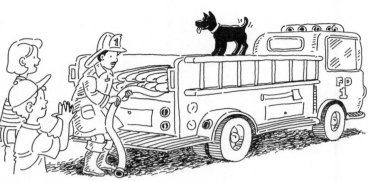

These sentences have adjectives that tell *what kind*. Circle the adjective that describes each underlined noun.

Example: The firefighters lifted the heavy hose.

1. That is a big fire truck.
2. The fire truck is red.
3. Brave firefighters fought the fire.
4. The old building caught fire quickly.
5. A large crowd gathered.
6. A black dog ran around the truck.
7. A firefighter patted the nervous dog.
8. It wagged its short tail.
9. The firefighters took the hungry animal to the firehouse.
10. We gave a loud cheer.

Name ____________________

LESSON 1 What Are Adjectives? ON YOUR OWN

Circle the adjective that describes each underlined noun. Then draw an arrow from the adjective to the noun it describes.

Example: Roberto is using a new rake.

1. Orange leaves fell from the trees.
2. It is a beautiful day.
3. Roberto is wearing a warm sweatshirt.
4. He rakes the leaves into a large pile.
5. A striped kitten chases a butterfly.
6. The pretty butterfly flies over the kitten.
7. The kitten swats at the butterfly with its tiny paw.
8. Roberto laughs at the little hunter.

Name ______________________

LESSON
2 More Adjectives TRY IT OUT

These sentences contain adjectives that tell *how many*. Circle the adjective that describes each underlined noun.

Example: The trip lasted (five) <u>days</u>.

1. The (three) <u>friends</u> went to New York City.
2. They visited (several) <u>museums</u>.
3. They saw (many) <u>paintings</u>.
4. The friends walked (seven) <u>blocks</u> to a park.
5. (Four) <u>squirrels</u> ran around a tree.
6. They took (some) <u>pictures</u> of buildings.
7. (One) <u>building</u> was the Empire State Building.
8. The friends took (two) <u>trips</u> to the Statue of Liberty.
9. They shopped at a (few) <u>stores</u>.
10. They bought (many) <u>presents</u> for their families.

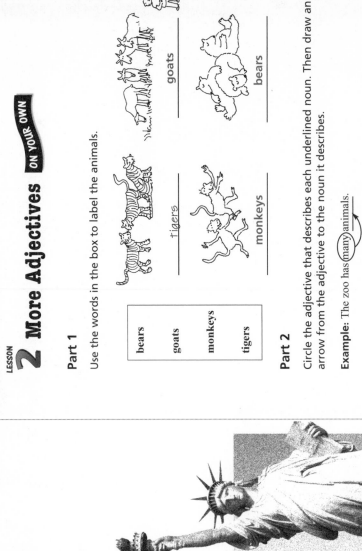

Name ______________________

LESSON
2 More Adjectives ON YOUR OWN

Part 1

Use the words in the box to label the animals.

bears
goats
monkeys
tigers

tigers

goats

monkeys

bears

Part 2

Circle the adjective that describes each underlined noun. Then draw an arrow from the adjective to the noun it describes.

Example: The zoo has (many) <u>animals</u>.

1. The zoo has (three) <u>tigers</u>.
2. (Some) <u>children</u> watched the monkeys.
3. (Four) <u>elephants</u> are standing under a tree.
4. A boy looked at (several) <u>goats</u>.
5. A (few) <u>bears</u> are sleeping.

Name ________

LESSON

3 Using *a, an,* and *the* TRY IT OUT

Choose the correct article in ( ) for each sentence. Write the article on the line.

Example: She is having __a__ (a, an) good time.

1. This is __a__ (a, an) pretty garden.
2. __The__ (A, The) red roses smell nice.
3. There is __an__ (a, an) oak tree in the garden.
4. __A__ (A, An) girl is swinging.
5. There is __an__ (a, an) old birdbath in the garden.
6. The girl is wearing __a__ (a, an) hat.
7. __The__ (The, A) hat belongs to her aunt.
8. It has __a__ (a, an) blue ribbon.

Name ________

LESSON

3 Using *a, an,* and *the* ON YOUR OWN

Choose the correct article in ( ) for each sentence. Write the article on the line.

Example: __The__ (An, The) girl's name is Annie.

1. Annie has __a__ (a, an) seeing-eye dog.
2. __The__ (A, The) dog's name is Tess.
3. Tess is __a__ (a, an) big dog.
4. Tess helps Annie cross __the__ (the, an) street.
5. __An__ (An, A) old truck waits for Tess and Annie to pass.
6. Annie is taking __an__ (a, an) art class.
7. She loves __the__ (a, the) class.
8. __The__ (A, The) teachers are nice.

Name ______________________

LESSON 4

Comparing with Adjectives TRY IT OUT

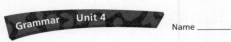

Sun, Mercury, Venus, Earth, Mars, Jupiter, Saturn, Uranus, Neptune, Pluto

Complete each sentence with the correct form of the adjective in ( ).

Example: Earth is ___smaller___ than Saturn. (small)

1. Jupiter is ___bigger___ than Earth. (big)
2. Which is the ___largest___ planet of all? (large)
3. Pluto is the ___smallest___ of all the planets. (small)
4. Is Saturn ___bigger___ than Uranus? (big)
5. Which planet is the ___closest___ of all to the Sun? (close)
6. Mars is ___nearer___ to Earth than Neptune. (near)

Name ______________________

LESSON 4

Comparing with Adjectives ON YOUR OWN

Part 1

Write a word from the box to label each body of the solar system.

Example: ___Sun___

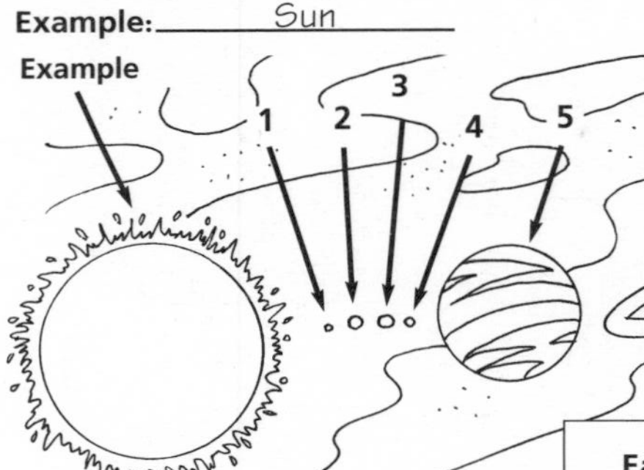

1. __________
2. __________
3. __________
4. __________
5. __________
6. __________
7. __________
8. __________
9. __________

Earth	Pluto
Jupiter	Uranus
Mars	Sun
Mercury	Venus
Neptune	Saturn

Part 2

Complete each sentence with the correct form of the adjective in ( ).

Example: A year on Pluto is ___longer___ than a year on Mars. (long)

1. Venus is the ___hottest___ planet of all. (hot)
2. It is ___closer___ to the Sun than Earth. (close)
3. Earth is ___nearer___ to the Sun than Saturn. (near)

Name ______________________

LESSON

5 What Are Adverbs?

Part 1

Underline the adverb in each sentence. Then write the adverb on the line.

Example: The girl calmly guides her horse around the track. calmly

1. The horses are walking slowly. slowly
2. The father put the saddle on easily. easily
3. The girl is sitting safely in the saddle. safely
4. She gently holds the reins. gently
5. The father and daughter ride regularly. regularly

Part 2

Write a sentence with an adverb about something you do regularly.

6. Answers will vary.

Name ______________________

LESSON

5 What Are Adverbs? ON YOUR OWN

These sentences contain adverbs that tell *how*. Underline the adverb in each sentence. Then write the adverb on the line.

Example: The horses ran swiftly across the meadow. swiftly

1. The horses are happily eating grass. happily
2. The sun is shining brightly. brightly
3. The mother horse calls softly to her foal. softly
4. The foal slowly walks to its mother. slowly
5. The wind is hardly blowing. hardly
6. The mother horse gently nuzzles her foal. gently
7. We watch quietly from a distance. quietly
8. Nervously the mother horse sniffs the air. Nervously

Grammar Unit 4 Name ____________________

LESSON 6

Other Kinds of Adverbs TRY IT OUT

Underline the adverb in each sentence. Decide whether it tells *when* or *where* the action takes place. Then write *when* or *where* for each sentence.

Example: My brother and I often help Grandmother. ___when___

1. Grandmother always loses things. ___when___
2. Yesterday she lost her glasses. ___when___
3. She looked around for them. ___where___
4. Then she asked my brother and me for help. ___when___
5. I looked here in the kitchen. ___where___
6. My brother looked upstairs. ___where___
7. We searched everywhere. ___where___
8. Next, my father helped. ___when___
9. He couldn't find the glasses anywhere. ___where___
10. Tomorrow Grandmother will buy new glasses. ___when___

Grammar Unit 4 Name ____________________

LESSON 6

Other Kinds of Adverbs ON YOUR OWN

Underline the adverb in each sentence. Decide whether it tells *when* or *where* the action takes place. Then write *when* or *where* for each sentence.

Example: We started our vacation yesterday. ___when___

1. Tomorrow we will visit the Washington Monument. ___when___
2. The White House is located nearby. ___where___
3. We walked to the Lincoln Memorial today. ___when___
4. Later we will drive by Capitol Hill. ___when___
5. Then we will have dinner at a hotel. ___when___
6. My uncle will meet us there. ___where___
7. My family and I really like it here. ___where___
8. I want to visit Washington, D.C., again. ___when___

Name ______________________

LESSON 7 Using *to, two,* and *too* TRY IT OUT

Complete each sentence with *to, two,* or *too.*

Example: I will take you __to__ the library.

1. Casey is __two__ years old.
2. This milk is __too__ old.
3. We take the bus __to__ school.
4. I want to go __too__.
5. Mr. Campbell has __two__ cats.
6. Please give the book __to__ Miguel.
7. The music is __too__ loud.
8. My mother is going __to__ the store.
9. I watched TV for __two__ hours last night.
10. I ate __too__ much ice cream!

Name ______________________

LESSON 7 Using *to, two,* and *too* ON YOUR OWN

Complete each sentence with *to, two,* or *too.*

Example: My mother takes the elevator __to__ the fifth floor.

1. Mother walks __to__ her office every day.
2. She eats lunch at __two__ o'clock.
3. Mother has __two__ pictures of me.
4. Sometimes she is __too__ busy.
5. She has __too__ many meetings.
6. I send e-mail messages __to__ my mother.
7. Mother talks __to__ me about her work.
8. One day, I will work in an office __too__.

Assessment Link

Name ______________________

Test Practice

Read each group of sentences. Choose the sentence that is written correctly. Circle the letter for that answer.

Example

A My dad has an computer.

B Mia bought a expensive printer.

C Ms. Carter uses a old typewriter.

(D) That computer is an unusual color.

1 A I have a uncle named Rocky.

(B) He went around the world in a boat.

C Did he bring you an present?

D He gave me a old statue.

2 F Maria is tallest than Kim.

(G) Vonda is shorter than Maria.

H Kim runs fastest than Vonda.

J Kim is the faster runner of the three.

3 **(A)** Mark gave milk to his cats.

B My cats like milk two.

C My too cats are Pokey and Max.

D Come two my house and see them.

4 **(F)** Today is hotter than yesterday.

G January was the colder month of the year.

H April is rainiest than July.

J October is usually cold than June.

5 A Let's go too the movies.

(B) I could eat two bags of popcorn!

C I like popcorn to.

D I'll race you too the car!

6 F Can you come with me too my great-grandfather's house?

G He has a old flag from the 1800s.

H The flag is even oldest than he is!

(J) He shows it proudly on special days.

7 A Ming is petting the horse careful.

B Softest a mother cat calls to her kitten.

(C) The grumpy goose squawked noisily.

D Some dogs run fastest than people.

UNIT 4 Test Practice

Assessment Link

Name ______________________

Test Practice *continued*

Read the passage all the way through once. Then look at the underlined parts. Decide if they need to be changed or if they are fine as they are. Choose the best answer from the choices given. Circle the letter of that answer.

My best friend is Nakisha Gray. She lives across the street from me. Nakisha and I have <u>growed</u> up together. Did you know that we have been classmates since first grade?

Example

A grew

B grow

(C) grown

D (No changes)

Math and spelling are our best subjects. Soccer is our favorite sport. Nakisha is a very fast <u>runner, but</u> I am a better goalie than she is.

8 A runner. But

B runner. but

C runner but

(D) (No changes)

You should see how <u>easy we pass</u> the ball to each other. The other team really doesn't have a chance!

9 F easier we pass

(G) easily we pass

H easiest we pass

J (No changes)

Nakisha is <u>the kinder</u> person I know. She is very funny and always cheers me up when I am sad.

10 **(A)** the kindest

B the most kindest

C the more kinder

D (No changes)

Name ______

LESSON 1 Correct Sentences TRY IT OUT

Part 1

Work together to label the parts of the computer. Draw an arrow from each label to the part it names.

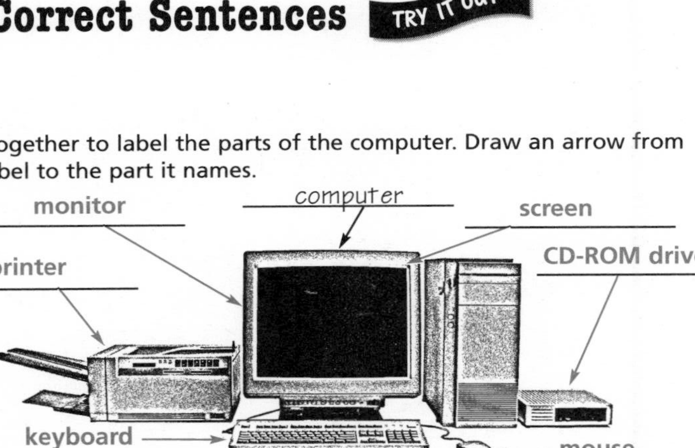

Part 2

Write each sentence correctly. Use capital letters and end marks.

Example: the games are on CD-ROMs

The games are on CD-ROMs.

1. this is my new computer
   This is my new computer.
2. do you have a computer
   Do you have a computer?
3. move the mouse carefully
   Move the mouse carefully.
4. this color printer is great
   This color printer is great!

Name ______

LESSON 1 Correct Sentences ON YOUR OWN

Write each sentence correctly.

Example: we have three computers in our classroom

We have three computers in our classroom.

1. is your school on the Internet
   Is your school on the Internet?
2. we love getting e-mail
   We love getting e-mail! (*or* .)
3. visit my school's Web site
   Visit my school's Web site.
4. our class wrote stories for the Web site
   Our class wrote stories for the Web site.
5. did you draw pictures too
   Did you draw pictures too?
6. the Internet has lots of information
   The Internet has lots of information.
7. computers make homework easy
   Computers make homework easy! (*or* .)
8. send me another e-mail soon
   Send me another e-mail soon.

Name ______________________

LESSON

2 Capitalizing Proper Nouns TRY IT OUT

Which nouns should have capital letters?
Write each sentence correctly.

Example: I saw denise at the store.

I saw Denise at the store.

1. On sunday we go to the movies.
   On Sunday we go to the movies.
2. We visited uncle bill.
   We visited Uncle Bill.
3. My birthday is in may.
   My birthday is in May.
4. My brother's name is eric w. mendez.
   My brother's name is Eric W. Mendez.
5. My aunt has a cat named fluffy.
   My aunt has a cat named Fluffy.
6. Are we going to see grandfather today?
   Are we going to see Grandfather today?
7. Elena's favorite holiday is labor day.
   Elena's favorite holiday is Labor Day.
8. The best day of the week is friday.
   The best day of the week is Friday.

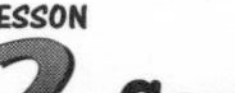

Name ______________________

LESSON

2 Capitalizing Proper Nouns ON YOUR OWN

Which nouns should have capital letters? Write each sentence correctly.

Example: What holiday is may 30?

What holiday is May 30?

1. When is new year's day?
   When is New Year's Day?
2. It is january 1.
   It is January 1.
3. Our school is closed on presidents' day.
   Our school is closed on Presidents' Day.
4. My father marches in a parade on memorial day.
   My father marches in a parade on Memorial Day.
5. After the parade, we visit uncle ernie.
   After the parade, we visit Uncle Ernie.
6. What foods do you eat on thanksgiving day?
   What foods do you eat on Thanksgiving Day?

Name ______________________

LESSON

3 Capitalizing Other Nouns TRY IT OUT

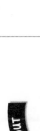

Which nouns should have capital letters? Write each sentence correctly.

Example: I live on redwood road.

I live on Redwood Road.

1. John lives in new mexico.
   John lives in New Mexico.
2. He lives in santa fe.
   He lives in Santa Fe.
3. John and Maria go to alameda elementary school.
   John and Maria go to Alameda Elementary School.
4. They like to visit bandelier national monument.
   They like to visit Bandelier National Monument.
5. Tai-Ming lives in california.
   Tai-Ming lives in California.
6. He can see the pacific ocean from his house.
   He can see the Pacific Ocean from his house.
7. Tai-Ming goes to school on powell street.
   Tai-Ming goes to school on Powell Street.
8. He likes to ride across the golden gate bridge.
   He likes to ride across the Golden Gate Bridge.

Name ______________________

LESSON

3 Capitalizing Other Nouns ON YOUR OWN

Which nouns should have capital letters? Write each sentence correctly.

Example: Have you ever seen the atlantic ocean?

Have you ever seen the Atlantic Ocean?

1. My neighbors are from mexico.
   My neighbors are from Mexico.
2. They lived in mexico city.
   They lived in Mexico City.
3. They live in new jersey now.
   They live in New Jersey now.
4. Their address is 207 long acre drive.
   Their address is 207 Long Acre Drive.
5. They want to visit canada.
   They want to visit Canada.
6. Min is from vietnam.
   Min is from Vietnam.
7. Now she lives in colorado.
   Now she lives in Colorado.
8. Min wants to go to yellowstone national park.
   Min wants to go to Yellowstone National Park.

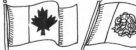

Grammar Unit 5 Name ______

LESSON

4 Abbreviations TRY IT OUT

Dr. Martha Hill
Hours: Mon.-Fri.
9:00-6:00

Part 1

Write each name and abbreviation correctly on the line.

Example: ms Garcia Ms. Garcia

1. sept Sept.
2. nov Nov.
3. dr Mark Richards Dr. Mark Richards
4. mon Mon.
5. mr Alex Sanchez Mr. Alex Sanchez
6. aug Aug.
7. fri Fri.
8. miss Tamaki Sato Miss Tamaki Sato
9. jan Jan.
10. mrs Samara Johnson Mrs. Samara Johnson

Part 2

Write the correct abbreviation for each day and month.

Example: Thursday Thurs.

11. February Feb.
12. December Dec.
13. Tuesday Tues.
14. April Apr.
15. Wednesday Wed.
16. March Mar.
17. Sunday Sun.
18. October Oct.

Grammar Unit 5 Name ______

LESSON

4 Abbreviations ON YOUR OWN

January February March April May June July August September October November December

Write the correct abbreviation for each day, month, and title. Write a check mark (✔) if the word or title does not have an abbreviation.

Example: Mister Welch Mr.

1. Saturday Sat.
2. January Jan.
3. June ✔
4. Tuesday Tues.
5. Doctor Amico Dr.
6. March Mar.
7. Miss Hamilton ✔
8. July ✔
9. Thursday Thurs.
10. May ✔

Name ______________________

LESSON 5 Book Titles TRY IT OUT

Write each book title correctly on the line. Add underlines and capital letters as needed.

Example: the wizard of oz

The Wizard of Oz

1. ramona and her mother
   Ramona and Her Mother
2. the waterfall
   The Waterfall
3. the first starry night
   The First Starry Night
4. chicken soup with rice
   Chicken Soup with Rice
5. the velveteen rabbit
   The Velveteen Rabbit
6. the garden of abdul gasazi
   The Garden of Abdul Gasazi

Name ______________________

LESSON 5 Book Titles ON YOUR OWN

Write each book title correctly.

Example: yunmi and Halmoni's Trip

Yunmi and Halmoni's Trip

1. Harry Potter and the sorcerer's stone
   Harry Potter and the Sorcerer's Stone
2. Poppa's New pants
   Poppa's New Pants
3. Rabbit races with turtle
   Rabbit Races with Turtle
4. Harold and the Purple Crayon
   Harold and the Purple Crayon
5. When Jo Louis won the Title
   When Jo Louis Won the Title
6. Mufaro's beautiful daughters
   Mufaro's Beautiful Daughters

Name ______________________

LESSON

6 Introductory Words TRY IT OUT

Read the sentences. Write *correct* if the sentence is correct. Write each incorrect sentence correctly. Add commas where they are needed.

Example: First the dog ran under the ladder.

First, the dog ran under the ladder.

1. Then the ladder tipped over.

correct

2. Next the paint can fell on the floor.

Next, the paint can fell on the floor.

3. Finally, the dog walked through the spilled paint.

correct

4. No the boy did not finish painting the door.

No, the boy did not finish painting the door.

5. Yes the boy and the dog need baths!

Yes, the boy and the dog need baths!

Name ______________________

LESSON

6 Introductory Words ON YOUR OWN

Part 1

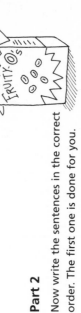

Read these instructions about preparing cereal. Are the steps in the right order? Write a number from 2 to 6 on the lines below to show the correct order. The first step has been numbered for you.

2 Second, you pour the cereal into a bowl.

4 Next, you pour the milk over the cereal.

1 First, you open the box of cereal.

6 Finally, you eat the cereal.

3 Third, you open a carton of milk.

5 Then you pick up a spoon.

Part 2

Now write the sentences in the correct order. The first one is done for you.

First, you open the box of cereal.

Second, you pour the cereal into a bowl.

Third, you open a carton of milk.

Next, you pour the milk over the cereal.

Then you pick up a spoon.

Finally, you eat the cereal.

Name ______________________

LESSON

7 Commas in a Series TRY IT OUT

Write each sentence correctly. Add commas where they are needed.

Example: There are banners balloons and presents.
There are banners, balloons, and presents.

1. Nicole Katie and Luis went to a party.
Nicole, Katie, and Luis went to a party.

2. The children had cake milk and sandwiches.
The children had cake, milk, and sandwiches.

3. They played danced and sang.
They played, danced, and sang.

4. Sara got toys clothes and books.
Sara got toys, clothes, and books.

5. Katie Luis and Sara are wearing party hats.
Katie, Luis, and Sara are wearing party hats.

Name ______________________

LESSON

7 Commas in a Series ON YOUR OWN

Write each sentence correctly. Add commas where they are needed.

Example: The relatives came in cars vans and buses.
The relatives came in cars, vans, and buses.

1. We ate corn chicken and watermelon.
We ate corn, chicken, and watermelon.

2. Aunt Mary Uncle Bill and Grandmother talked.
Aunt Mary, Uncle Bill, and Grandmother talked.

3. Joel brought balls bats and gloves.
Joel brought balls, bats, and gloves.

4. Joel Missy and Ken played ball.
Joel, Missy, and Ken played ball.

5. My family has a picnic every June July and August.
My family has a picnic every June, July, and August.

Grammar Unit 5

Name ______

LESSON

8 Quotation Marks TRY IT OUT

Write each sentence correctly. Add quotation marks where they are needed.

Example: Wing said, I like to play baseball.

Wing said, "I like to play baseball."

1. Juan said, Good morning!
   Juan said, "Good morning!"
2. When will we eat lunch? asked Fran.
   "When will we eat lunch?" asked Fran.
3. Tomo said, I'm wearing my new sneakers.
   Tomo said, "I'm wearing my new sneakers."
4. Carl said, Your book report is great!
   Carl said, "Your book report is great!"
5. Lisa asked, Can you go to the library with me?
   Lisa asked, "Can you go to the library with me?"
6. I have ballet class today, Erica answered.
   "I have ballet class today," Erica answered.
7. Marta said, I will go with you.
   Marta said, "I will go with you."
8. Mr. Potts said, Please get out your homework.
   Mr. Potts said, "Please get out your homework."

Grammar Unit 5

Name ______

LESSON

8 Quotation Marks ON YOUR OWN

Write each sentence correctly. Add quotation marks where they are needed.

Example: Paul said, I can chop down two trees at once.

Paul said, "I can chop down two trees at once."

1. Paul asked, Are you hungry?
   Paul asked, "Are you hungry?"
2. Babe answered, I'm always hungry.
   Babe answered, "I'm always hungry."
3. What do you want to eat? asked Paul.
   "What do you want to eat?" asked Paul.
4. Babe replied, I want one hundred ears of corn!
   Babe replied, "I want one hundred ears of corn!"
5. Paul said, That is a lot of corn.
   Paul said, "That is a lot of corn."

Name ____________________

LESSON

9 More About Quotation Marks TRY IT OUT

Write each sentence correctly. Add a comma, a capital letter, an end mark, and quotation marks to each sentence.

Example: Ping asked do you like to fly kites

Ping asked, "Do you like to fly kites?"

1. Jason said here is my new kite

   Jason said, "Here is my new kite."

2. Ping asked is it windy enough

   Ping asked, "Is it windy enough?"

3. Cody said let's go to the park

   Cody said, "Let's go to the park."

4. Ping asked do you have enough string

   Ping asked, "Do you have enough string?"

5. Jason said let's run fast

   Jason said, "Let's run fast."

6. Cody shouted be careful of the trees

   Cody shouted, "Be careful of the trees!"

Name ____________________

LESSON

9 More About Quotation Marks ON YOUR OWN

Write each sentence correctly. Add a comma, a capital letter, an end mark, or quotation marks to each sentence.

Example: Cam said I ruined my cup

Cam said, "I ruined my cup!"

1. Mr. Gomez said, we can fix it.

   Mr. Gomez said, "We can fix it."

2. Tiana said "I want to make a bowl"

   Tiana said, "I want to make a bowl."

3. Kirk asked can I paint my dish?

   Kirk asked, "Can I paint my dish?"

4. Cam asked, "May I have some more clay

   Cam asked, "May I have some more clay?"

5. Kirk exclaimed this is fun

   Kirk exclaimed, "This is fun!"

Name ______________________

Test Practice

Choose the best way to write the underlined part of each sentence. Circle the letter for that answer. If there is no mistake, circle the letter for the last answer.

Example: The class picnic is on apr 27.

- (A) Apr. 27
- B apr. 27
- C Apr 27
- D (No mistakes)

1 Where is south county school.

- A South County School.
- B south county school?
- (C) South County School?
- D (No mistakes)

2 I saw dr Kelly today.

- F dr. Kelly
- (G) Dr. Kelly
- H Dr Kelly
- J (No mistakes)

3 I really enjoyed the book danger on midnight river.

- A Danger on midnight river
- B Danger On Midnight River
- (C) Danger on Midnight River
- D (No mistakes)

4 We need butter, milk, and eggs.

- F butter milk and eggs
- G butter, milk and, eggs
- H butter milk, and eggs
- (J) (No mistakes)

5 Chan's birthday is sep 28, 1993.

- A sep. 28
- (B) Sept. 28
- C Sep. 28
- D (No mistakes)

6 No I don't have a pen.

- (F) No, I don't
- G No. I don't
- H No I, don't
- J (No mistakes)

7 Mom said take off your shoes.

- A said "take off your shoes."
- B said, "Take off your shoes".
- (C) said, "Take off your shoes."
- D (No mistakes)

Name ______________________

Test Practice *continued*

Read the passage and look at the numbered, underlined parts. Choose the correct way to write each underlined part. If the part is already correct, choose the last answer, "Correct as it is." Circle the letter for the answer you choose.

In april my family (Example) went to mustang island state park (8) in Texas. A mustang is a wild horse. People brought horses to the island in the 1800s, Did (9) I enjoy the park? Yes, I had a great time (10). We went swimming hiking and fishing (11) along the beach. The island also has small animals and sand dunes to explore.

"When can we visit again (12) I asked my parents.

Example

- A In april my Family
- (B) In April my family
- C In April my Family
- D Correct as it is

8
- (A) Mustang Island State Park
- B Mustang Island state park
- C Mustang island state park
- D Correct as it is

9
- (F) in the 1800s. Did
- G in the 1800s? Did
- H in the 1800s, did
- J Correct as it is

10
- A Yes I had a great time.
- B Yes, I, had a great time.
- C Yes I had, a great time.
- (D) Correct as it is

11
- F swimming, hiking, fishing
- (G) swimming, hiking, and fishing
- H swimming, hiking and fishing
- J Correct as it is

12
- A "When can we visit again?
- B "When can we visit again,"
- (C) "When can we visit again?"
- D Correct as it is

Name ______

LESSON 1

Subject Pronouns TRY IT OUT

Underline the subject pronouns. Then write each sentence on the line.

Example: She is wearing a raincoat.

She is wearing a raincoat.

1. I like the way the sky looks.
   I like the way the sky looks.
2. Do you like the rain?
   Do you like the rain?
3. They are walking in the rain.
   They are walking in the rain.
4. Did she have a polka dot umbrella?
   Did she have a polka dot umbrella?
5. He jumped in a puddle.
   He jumped in a puddle.

Name ______

LESSON 1

Subject Pronouns ON YOUR OWN

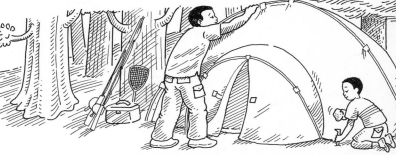

Replace the underlined word or words in each sentence with a pronoun. Then write the new sentence on the line. Remember to use a capital letter if the pronoun is at the beginning of the sentence.

Example: Father and I will stay home this time. *We*

We will stay home this time.

1. James and Paul went camping. **They**
   They went camping.
2. The tent is big. **It**
   It is big.
3. Are the trees very old? **they**
   Are they very old?
4. James loves to go fishing. **He**
   He loves to go fishing.
5. Did my mother bake cookies for the boys? **she**
   Did she bake cookies for the boys?

Name ______________________

LESSON

2 Pronouns and Verbs TRY IT OUT

Choose the correct verb form in ( ) to complete each sentence. Write the verb on the line.

Example: We help Mom make breakfast. (help, helps)

1. I love eggs for breakfast! (love, loves)

2. He cracks the eggs. (crack, cracks)

3. They drip onto the table. (drips, drip)

4. She cooks the omelets. (cook, cooks)

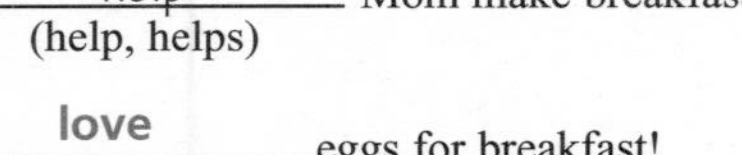

5. We eat breakfast quickly. (eats, eat)

6. Now, you clean the counter! (clean, cleans)

Name ______________________

LESSON

2 Pronouns and Verbs ON YOUR OWN

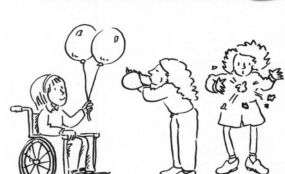

Choose the correct verb form in ( ) to complete each sentence. Write the verb on the line.

Example: They blow up the balloons. (blow up, blows up)

1. She holds two balloons. (holds, hold)

2. You pop a balloon. (pops, pop)

3. He loses one balloon. (lose, loses)

4. It floats in the air. (float, floats)

5. They enjoy playing with balloons. (enjoy, enjoys)

6. We like balloons too! (likes, like)

Grammar Unit 6

Name ______

LESSON 3

Object Pronouns — TRY IT OUT

Underline the object pronoun in each sentence.

Example: The director is pointing at <u>you</u>.

1. Mrs. Shepard told <u>us</u> to come early.
2. We were on the stage with <u>her</u>.
3. Mrs. Shepard gave a part to <u>him</u>.
4. She helped <u>them</u> practice.
5. The play was a success for <u>her</u>.
6. Everyone loved <u>it</u>!
7. Did you see <u>me</u> on stage?
8. Yes, I saw <u>you</u>.

Grammar Unit 6

Name ______

LESSON 3

Object Pronouns — ON YOUR OWN

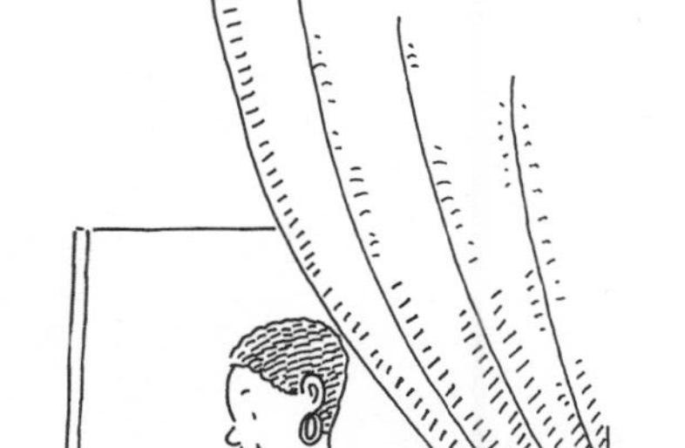

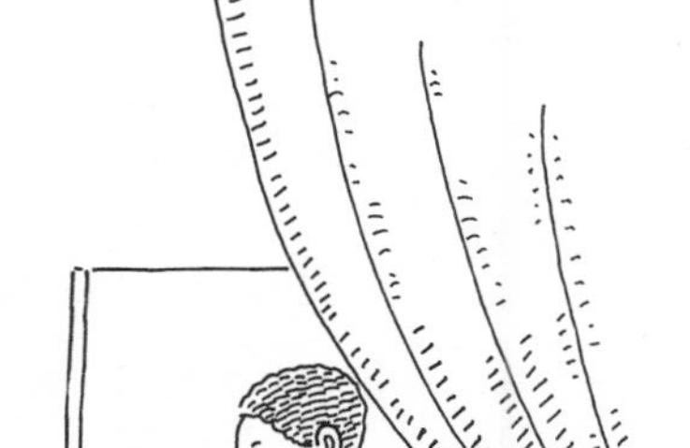

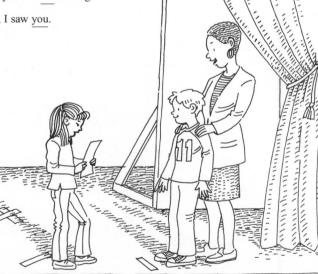

Part 1

Replace the underlined word or words in each sentence with a pronoun. Then write the pronoun on the line.

Example: I went to the football game with <u>Dad and Robert</u>. them

1. Dad told <u>Robert and me</u> to bring hats and mittens. us
2. I gave my warmest scarf to <u>Robert</u>. him
3. Emma sat with <u>Robert and me</u>. us
4. She liked <u>the marching bands</u>. them
5. Kayla waved to <u>Emma</u>. her
6. Did you see <u>the game</u>? it

Part 2

Now complete these sentences. Use at least one object pronoun in each sentence.

7. Our teacher asked Answers will vary.
8. Mom helped ______

Name ______________________

LESSON 4 Using *I* and *me* TRY IT OUT

Choose the correct words in ( ) to complete each sentence. Write the words on the line.

Example: Kim and I are good friends.
(Kim and I, I and Kim)

1. Kim and I went to the store.
(Kim and I, I and Kim)

2. Mom came with Kim and me.
(Kim and me, me and Kim)

3. Kim and I looked at shoes and CDs.
(Me and Kim, Kim and I)

4. Kim and I bought some CDs.
(Kim and I, Kim and me)

5. Mom bought ice cream for Kim and me.
(Kim and me, me and Kim)

6. Then Kim and I had a big surprise.
(I and Kim, Kim and I)

7. Mom took Kim and me to a movie!
(Kim and I, Kim and me)

8. Kim and I thanked Mom for a great day!
(Kim and I, I and Kim)

Name ______________________

LESSON 4 Using *I* and *me* ON YOUR OWN

Choose the correct word or words in ( ) to complete each sentence.

Example: My sister and I got up early.
(My sister and I, I and my sister)

1. Lindsay and I made breakfast for Grandma.
(Lindsay and I, I and Lindsay)

2. I like to make pancakes.
(I, Me)

3. Lindsay helped me with the batter.
(I, me)

4. Lindsay and I served Grandma breakfast in bed.
(Me and Lindsay, Lindsay and I)

5. Grandma gave Lindsay and me a big hug.
(me and Lindsay, Lindsay and me)

Name ____________________

LESSON 5

Possessive Pronouns TRY IT OUT

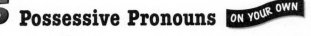

Underline the possessive pronoun in each sentence. Then write the sentence on the line.

Example: His name is David.

His name is David.

1. What is your name?
   What is your name?
2. I don't know their names.
   I don't know their names.
3. Her bicycle is red.
   Her bicycle is red.
4. Where is my bicycle?
   Where is my bicycle?
5. His cat is big and gray.
   His cat is big and gray.
6. Its name is Whiskers.
   Its name is Whiskers.
7. Did John do his math homework?
   Did John do his math homework?
8. We did our homework yesterday.
   We did our homework yesterday.

Name ____________________

LESSON 5

Possessive Pronouns ON YOUR OWN

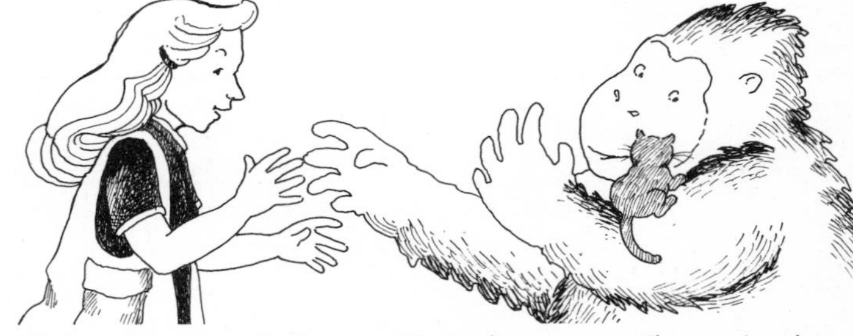

Underline the possessive pronoun in each sentence. Then write the sentence on the line.

Example: Does Koko like her kitten?

Does Koko like her kitten?

1. This is her kitten.
   This is her kitten.
2. His name is Smoky.
   His name is Smoky.
3. Her trainer watches them.
   Her trainer watches them.
4. Smoky looks like my kitten.
   Smoky looks like my kitten.
5. Michael and Koko play with their trainer.
   Michael and Koko play with their trainer.
6. We will tell our friends about the gorillas.
   We will tell our friends about the gorillas.

Name ______________________

LESSON

6 Contractions TRY IT OUT

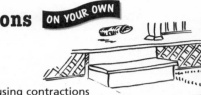

We have to clean the attic next. Come on, it'll be fun!

Write the contraction for each pair of words.

Example: I have ___I've___

1. she is ___she's___

2. they will ___they'll___

3. you are ___you're___

4. we have ___we've___

5. it is ___it's___

6. we will ___we'll___

7. he will ___he'll___

8. he has ___he's___

9. they have ___they've___

10. I will ___I'll___

11. she has ___she's___

12. you have ___you've___

13. he is ___he's___

14. we are ___we're___

15. I am ___I'm___

16. they are ___they're___

17. you will ___you'll___

18. it will ___it'll___

19. she will ___she'll___

20. it has ___it's___

Name ______________________

LESSON

6 Contractions ON YOUR OWN

Rewrite the sentences using contractions for the underlined words.

Example: I will write a story.

I'll write a story.

1. He is a good worker.

He's a good worker.

2. We will help him.

We'll help him.

3. She has studied English for two years.

She's studied English for two years.

4. I think they have moved.

I think they've moved.

5. He will be ten years old next month.

He'll be ten years old next month.

6. We have never been to New York City.

We've never been to New York City.

7. Do you think he is tired?

Do you think he's tired?

8. They are my favorite soccer players.

They're my favorite soccer players.

 Name ____________

LESSON 7

Using *there*, *their*, and *they're* TRY IT OUT

They're over there.

Choose the correct word in ( ) to complete each sentence. Write the word on the line.

Example: Their (Their, There) backpacks are on the floor.

1. The book is there (there, they're) on the table.
2. Their (Their, They're) work is always good.
3. They're (There, They're) watching a baseball game.
4. Where are their (there, their) bicycles?
5. The bicycles are over there (there, they're) by the tree.
6. They're (They're, Their) doing homework in the library.
7. Their (They're, Their) paintings are pretty.
8. I think that they're (they're, their) the best singers.

 Name ____________

LESSON 7

Using *there*, *their*, and *they're* ON YOUR OWN

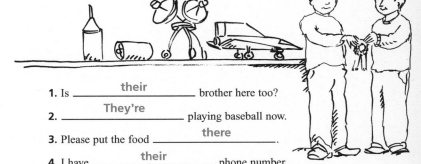

Complete each sentence with *there*, *their*, or *they're*. Write the correct word on the line. Use a capital letter if necessary.

Example: Their project is great!

1. Is their brother here too?
2. They're playing baseball now.
3. Please put the food there.
4. I have their phone number.
5. They're visiting some friends.
6. I went there to buy some books.
7. Their science project won first prize.
8. Please sit over there.
9. Do you know where they're going?
10. Are their cats black and white?
11. Are there any more cookies?
12. They're going to take the bus home.

Assessment Link

Name ______________________

Test Practice

Choose the best way to write the underlined part of each sentence. Circle the letter for that answer. If there is no mistake, circle the letter for the last answer.

Example: Keiko and me made cookies.

- A Me and Keiko
- (B) Keiko and I
- C I and Keiko
- D (No mistakes)

1 Grandma made sweaters for Pat and I.

- A me and Pat
- B I and Pat
- (C) Pat and me
- D (No mistakes)

2 What are they're names?

- F they are
- (G) their
- H there
- J (No mistakes)

3 They plays together every day.

- (A) play
- B playing
- C has played
- D (No mistakes)

4 What is you're favorite color?

- F you
- G you are
- (H) your
- J (No mistakes)

5 Pablo and I went to the movies.

- A Pablo and me
- B Me and Pablo
- C I and Pablo
- (D) (No mistakes)

6 I saw a movie star over their.

- F they're
- (G) there
- H they
- J (No mistakes)

7 Its a good day for a hike.

- (A) It's
- B Its'
- C It
- D (No mistakes)

UNIT 6 Test Practice

Assessment Link

Name ______________________

Test Practice *continued*

Look at each underlined part of the paragraph. Find the correct way to write the underlined part in each numbered line. Circle the letter of that answer. If the part is already correct, circle the letter for the last answer, "Correct as it is."

(Example) Uranus Neptune and Pluto are the last planets of our solar
(8) system. There very cold because the Sun is too far away to warm them.
(9) Scientists have careful gathered data from the *Voyager II* space probe
(10) about these distant planets we now know that Uranus has fifteen
(11) moons, and Neptune has eight moons. Neptunes largest moon is
(12) Triton. Scientists believe that Triton is the coldest place in the solar system. Pluto has only one moon. It is named Charon.

Example

- (A) Uranus, Neptune, and Pluto
- B Uranus Neptune, and Pluto
- C Uranus, Neptune and, Pluto
- D Correct as it is

8
- A Their
- (B) They're
- C There are
- D Correct as it is

9
- F carefuller
- (G) carefully
- H carefullest
- J Correct as it is

10
- A planets, we
- B planets. we
- (C) planets. We
- D Correct as it is

11
- (F) Neptune's
- G Neptunes'
- H Neptunes's
- J Correct as it is

12
- A cold
- B most coldest
- C colder
- (D) Correct as it is

Section 3: Resources

Key Terms and Definitions

Beginning/Preproduction is the stage in language learning in which students understand verbal cues but cannot produce verbal responses.

Bilingual means to be proficient in two languages.

Communicative competence is the knowledge of the words, phrases, and conventions speakers use to communicate in socially and culturally appropriate ways.

Early Production/Speech Emergent is the stage in language learning in which students understand verbal cues and are beginning to produce verbal responses.

English as a foreign language (EFL) refers to the teaching of English in a country where the primary language is a language other than English.

English as a second language (ESL) refers to the field of study as well as to the design and development of course materials, classes, and programs of study associated with the teaching of English as a second language. ESL is used to refer to the teaching of English in any country where English is the primary language of communication.

False beginners are students who have studied English but have limited ability to communicate their ideas.

First language is the first language (the student) learned. It is also referred to as the student's native language.

Four skills refers to the skills of reading, writing, listening, and speaking.

Integrated syllabus is one that integrates the four skills of reading, writing, listening, and speaking within a planned syllabus of grammar and other language skills needed for successful social interaction.

Intermediate/Advanced is the stage in language learning in which students understand verbal cues, can respond verbally, and have gained some proficiency in both reading and writing.

L1 is the short form for first language.

L2 is the short form for second language.

Native language/home language/primary language is the language spoken prior to coming to the United States, or currently spoken within the home other than English.

Oral/aural competence refers to listening and speaking abilities, including pronunciation.

Previewing activities are those done in preparation for the actual lesson, such as practicing new vocabulary, talking about illustrations, or examining titles in a selection.

Productive language is the language students understand and can use in their speaking or writing.

Receptive language is the language students may understand from context, but are not yet able to use or expected to use in their own communication.

Scaffolding is the framework or background a student uses to understand information. Students are helped to build a scaffolding by doing previewing activities that develop background and activate prior knowledge. These activities build a foundation, making it easier for students to understand new material.

Second language is the second language someone learns.

Key Terms and Definitions *continued*

Sheltered English is a teaching approach in which students develop proficiency in a subject matter largely due to the modifications the teacher makes in the presentation. The teacher utilizes supports such as demonstrations, visuals, simplified English, and graphic organizers to make the subject matter easier to grasp for the English language learner.

Student acquiring English is the term used in Houghton Mifflin English. A student acquiring English is anyone who is still in the process of acquiring English and who speaks a language other than English as the **first language.** The primary language may also be called the **home language, primary language,** or **native language.** These terms are all used interchangeably.

Target language is the language a student is trying to learn.

Teachers of English to Speakers of Other Languages (TESOL), with its headquarters in Washington, DC, is the professional organization for professionals in the fields of ESL/EFL.

Total Physical Response (TPR) is a technique for language teaching developed by James Asher. It is especially useful in the early stages of learning because students respond to verbal and visual cues such as "Stand up" or "Point to the book" without speaking.

Positive Transfer

Not every aspect of every language differs from English. Those languages that share the closest historical ties with English naturally have many areas of positive transfer. One of the most important areas of positive transfer is the alphabet that we share with many of the European languages. The following identifies some general areas of positive language transfer.

- A **shared alphabet** gives students an advantage over those who must learn a new alphabet.
- The **shared historical development** of the European languages allows students to make analogies with their own language.
- **Cognates** allow students to make fairly accurate guesses about meaning even though false cognates are just as likely to mislead students.
- **Similar sounds** occur in many languages.
- Many **language structures** in English occur in other languages as well.
- Some **writing conventions** apply in related languages.
- Languages tend to use **figurative language** to express similar ideas even though the exact words will vary considerably.

Language Guide to Transfer Errors

The following language guide sets out several problem areas for students acquiring English. It shows grammatical features *(column 1)* of specific languages *(column 2)* that when transferred to English lead to an error *(column 3)*. The guide covers neither all linguistic problem areas nor all languages; that would take volumes. Rather, it lists a selection, with the aim of being useful and practical. Use the guide to raise your awareness about languages.

LANGUAGE FEATURES	LANGUAGES																						SAMPLE TRANSFER ERRORS IN ENGLISH
	Arabic	Bengali	Chinese	Farsi	French	German	Gujarati	Greek	Haitian Creole	Hebrew	Hindi	Japanese	Korean	Portuguese	Russian	Spanish	Swahili	Tagalog	Thai	Turkish	Urdu	Vietnamese	
ARTICLES																							**ARTICLES**
No articles			●	●								●			●		●		●		●		*Book is on table.* *Sun is hot.*
No indefinite article with profession	●				●				●			●	●									●	*He is student.* *She doctor.*
Definite article with days, months, places, idioms	●																						*She is at the home.* *They will come in the July.*
Definite article used for generalization					●	●		●						●		●							*The little children always like the ice cream.* *The swimming is good exercise.*
No article for generalization with singular noun									●														*Bird can fly.*
Definite article used with proper noun					●	●		●						●		●							*My dentist is the Doctor Smith.*
No definite article											●									●			*Store on corner is closed.*
No indefinite article (uses *one* for *a* and depends on context)													●										*He found one book.*
VERBS AND VERBALS																							**VERBS AND VERBALS**
Be can be omitted	●		●						●						●								*She studying now.* *He always happy.*

No progressive forms					●	●		●							●								*They still play now.* *When I called, she studied.*
No tense inflections			●																●			●	*He have a good time yesterday.* *When she was little, she always walk to school.*
No inflections for person and number			●									●	●		●				●				*The school have a good soccer team.*
Past perfect formed with *be*	●																						*They were arrived.*
Different tense boundaries from English	●		●	●	●				●														*I study English for a year.* *He has left yesterday.*
Different limits for passive voice												●	●		●				●			●	*They were taken our lunches.* *My name base on Chinese characters.* *An accident was happened.*
No *-ing* (gerund)/infinitive distinction	●		●	●	●			●						●		●						●	*She avoids to see him.* *I enjoy to play baseball.*
Infinitive not used to express purpose													●										*I went out for seeing a movie.*
Overuse of progressive forms											●										●		*I am wanting to leave now.*
WORD ORDER AND SENTENCE STRUCTURE																							**WORD ORDER AND SENTENCE STRUCTURE**
Verb precedes subject	●									●					●	●		●					*Good grades received every student in the class.* *Spanish: optional*
Verb–subject order in dependent clause					●				●														*I knew what would say the teacher.*
Verb last		●				●					●	●	●							●			*. . .when the teacher the papers collected.* *German: in dependent clause*
Coordination favored over subordination	●																						*Frequent use of* and *and* so
Relative clause or restrictive phrase precedes noun it modifies			●									●	●		●								*The entered in the contest students. . .* *He gave me a too difficult for me book.*
Adverb can occur between verb and object or before verb					●				●												●		*I like very much oranges.* *She watched carefully the baby.* *He slowly runs.* *Urdu: before verb*
That clause rather than infinitive	●				●				●		●				●	●							*I want that you stay.* *Father wants that he try harder.*
Inversion of subject and verb rare			●																				*She is leaving and so I am.*

LANGUAGE FEATURES	Arabic	Bengali	Chinese	Farsi	French	German	Gujarati	Greek	Haitian Creole	Hebrew	Hindi	Japanese	Korean	Portuguese	Russian	Spanish	Swahili	Tagalog	Thai	Turkish	Urdu	Vietnamese	SAMPLE TRANSFER ERRORS IN ENGLISH
WORD ORDER AND SENTENCE STRUCTURE ***continued***																							**WORD ORDER AND SENTENCE STRUCTURE** ***continued***
Conjunctions occur in pairs			●	●																		●	*Although she is rich, but she drives an old car.* *Even if I had time, I would also not go.*
Subject can be omitted (especially pronoun)			●									●				●			●				*Is raining.* *Studied last night.*
Commas set off a dependent clause						●									●								*He knows, that we called.*
No equivalent of *there is/there are*												●	●	●	●	●			●				*This book says four reasons to eat beans.* *In the park has many trees.* *Thai: uses adverb of place and have*
NOUNS, PRONOUNS, ADJECTIVES, ADVERBS																							**NOUNS, PRONOUNS, ADJECTIVES, ADVERBS**
Personal pronouns restate subject	●						●									●							*My grandfather he lives in California.*
No human/nonhuman distinction for relative pronoun *(who/which)*	●			●	●										●	●			●				*Here is the new student which you met her last week.* *The people which arrived. . .*
Pronoun object added at end of relative clause	●			●						●													*The house that I used to live in it is big.*
No distinction between subject and object forms of pronouns			●				●						●			●			●				*I gave the books to she.*
Nouns and adjectives have the same form			●									●											*She is very beauty woman.* *They felt very safety on the bus.*
No distinction between *he/she, his/her*		●		●			●												●				*My sister dropped his lunch.*
No plural form after a number			●	●									●										*Four new shirt. . .*
No plural (or optional) forms of nouns			●									●	●						●				*Several good book. . .*
No relative pronouns													●										*The book is on the table is mine.*
Adjectives show number					●											●							*I have helpfuls friends.*
Double negatives are routinely used																●							*They don't know nothing.*
Pronoun subjects can be omitted																●			●				*My mother complained when saw the mess.*